The Leprechaun Book

The Leprechaun Book

Edited by Mairtin O'Griofa

Illustrated by Sheila Kern

A Sterling/Main Street Book
Sterling Publishing Co., Inc.   New York

The excerpt from Carolyn White's *A History of
Irish Fairies,* beginning on page 24, is reprinted
with the permission of The Mercier Press, Cork, Ireland.

Library of Congress Cataloging-in-Publication Data.

The leprechaun book / edited by Mairtin O'Griofa
     p.   cm.
  Includes index.
  ISBN 0-8069-0829-7
  1. Fantastic fiction, English—Irish authors. 2. Folklore—
Ireland—Fiction. 3. Fairy tales—Ireland. 4. Leprechauns—
Fiction. I. O'Griofa, Mairtin.
PR8876.5.F35L47 1994
823'.0876608375—dc20   94-26080
                                                                                    CIP

Designed by John Murphy
Typeset by Upper Case Limited, Cork, Ireland.

10   9   8   7   6   5   4   3   2   1

A Sterling/Main Street Book

Published in 1994 by Sterling Publishing Company, Inc.
387 Park Avenue South, New York, N.Y. 10016
© 1994 by Sterling Publishing Company, Inc.
Distributed in Canada by Sterling Publishing
c/o Canadian Manda Group, One Atlantic Avenue, Suite 105
Toronto, Ontario, Canada M6K 3E7
Distributed in Great Britain and Europe by Cassell PLC
Villiers House, 41/47 Strand, London WC2N 5JE, England
Distributed in Australia by Capricorn Link (Australia) Pty Ltd.
P.O. Box 6651, Baulkham Hills, Business Centre, NSW 2153,
Australia

Manufactured in the United States of America
All rights reserved

ISBN 0-8069-0829-7

Contents

Introduction   6

Lepracaun, Cluricaun, Far Darrig
by W. B. Yeats   11

The Leprechawn *by D. R. McAnally, Jr.*   12

Leprechauns, Cluricauns, Far Darrigs
by Caroline White   24

The Field of Boliauns *by Joseph Jacobs*   31

Master and Man *by Thomas Crofton Croker*   35

Teig O'Kane and the Corpse *by Douglas Hyde*   44

The Haunted Cellar *by Thomas Crofton Croker*   62

Far Darrig in Donegal *by Letitia Maclintock*   71

The Lepracaun; or, Fairy Shoemaker
by William Allingham   76

From the Crock of Gold *by James Stephens*   79

The Gollan *by A. E. Coppard*   91

The Fairy Shoe *by Edith Somerville*   100

Darby O'Gill and the Leprechaun
by Herminie Kavanagh   107

Index   127

Introduction

IF YOU think a leprechaun is anything like the cute little green fellow found on cereal boxes or under Finian's rainbow, think again. You'll rarely find a leprechaun wearing such a serene color as green. He wears red, the color of passion and violence, or sometimes even brown or gray to camouflage him from the tree trunks under which he lives and hides. And he's much too busy cobbling shoes and guarding fairy treasure hoards to dance about, telling jokes and singing songs.

Gleaned from centuries of Irish writing on the elusive and solitary creature, the pages that follow tell the composite story of the leprechaun—"composite" because no two writers have ever described the diminutive fellow in exactly the same way—from the feisty fairy's origin as the defective offspring of beautiful parents to his love for smelly stumps of pipes called *dudeens* and his guzzling of beer from earthen jugs.

Far from being the beloved "wee man" of greeting cards, leprechauns are usually portrayed as ugly, stunted creatures, as tall as boys of ten or twelve—with wizened faces like dried apples. Foul-mouthed, discontented drunkards, they serve a multitude of purposes for their fairy relatives and take these duties with earnest seriousness as they wage war on greedy mortals who attempt, and always fail, to outsmart them.

The Leprechaun Book examines the daily life of the leprechaun in lore and legend and outlines the activities of his lesser-known first cousins, the cluricaun and the far darrig (red man), whom some believe to be guises of the leprechaun himself in drunken or malicious moods. The book is divided roughly into two parts, the first quoting the words of three experts in their attempt to atomize these fairy "atomies" and the second offering a selection of the best leprechaun stories ever told. Along the way will be references to leprechaun relics on view in Ireland, including the famous fairy shoe of Edith Somerville, co-author of *The Irish R.M.*

Through the years, many folklorists and literary writers have attempted to describe the traits and functions of the leprechaun, among them the great Irish poet William Butler Yeats (1865-1939), whose concise words in *Irish Fairy and Folk Tales* form the opening chapter of this book. Yeats was among the first to divide the denizens of the fairy race into two forms—the trooping fairies and the solitary fairies. The trooping fairies, as their names implies, delight in company, while the solitary fairies prefer to be left by themselves and separate from one another. The leprechaun is the best known member of the second group.

In reviewing David Rice McAnally, Jr.'s *Irish Wonders* (1888), Yeats wrote that "the chapter on the leprechaun contains the most minute descriptions of that creature extant." McAnally's famed chapter is reprinted here in its entirety and is the lodestone from which many modern writers have mined much of their information about our elusive wee fellows. Many of the leprechaun stories told by McAnally are written in a dialect which may appear to modern readers to be somewhat "stage-Irishy" but is nonetheless anything but patronizing or condescending. (Several selections in *The Leprechaun Book* are written in dialect attempting—some successfully, some not—to capture the sounds and sentence structure of Irish-English.)

McAnally's chapter on the leprechaun is followed by the best modern synthesis of the life and times of the leprechaun and his kin, that contained in Carolyn White's *A History of Irish Fairies* (1976), a delightfully concise summary of everything anyone might possibly want to know about the "little people." The section on leprechauns, cluricauns, and far darrigs is reprinted here with the kind permission of The Mercier Press, Cork.

The reader will recognize in the three preceding pieces three different spellings of "leprechaun"—lepracaun, leprachawn, and the more common leprechaun. These orthographic variations reflect not a confusion of sources but the vagaries of transliterating into English what is after all an Irish word!

With the central information gleaned from Yeats, McAnally, and White as background, *The Leprechaun Book* offers a selection of outstanding stories of leprechauns, cluricauns, and far darrigs, some of them elaborating on the fairy traits described by folklorists, and others created from the whole cloth of the writers' imagination.

"The Field of Boliauns," the first of the stories, is from *Celtic Fairy Tales* by Joseph Jacobs (1854-1916), a student of world folklore. Determined to find the most authentic versions of local stories, he included in his two-volume work only those which had been related by speakers of Scottish and Irish Gaelic, Welsh, and Cornish. "The Field of Boliauns," he writes, was originally told of a cluricaun, but was also told in the leprechaun version rendered here.

Thomas Crofton Croker (1798-1854), author of *Fairy Legends and Traditions of the South of Ireland,* is one of the most distinguished of all Irish folklore collectors. "Master and Man," taken from that multivolume work, may be about leprechauns, but the creature's fondness for drink suggests that he might very well be a cluricaun. The story is as moralistic as it is fanciful.

The supernatural creatures in "Teig O'Kane and the Corpse" by Douglas Hyde (1862-1949) are identified by W. B. Yeats, in whose *Irish Fairy and Folk Tales* the story first appeared, as trooping fairies. Other commentators call them solitary. The reader is free to decide for himself, although the traits of the far darrig will come immediately to mind.

There will be no question about the identity of the tippling creature in Thomas Crofton Croker's *The Haunted Cellar*. It is of course a cluricaun.

"Far Darrig in Donegal" by the unsung Letitia Maclintic, who remains unlisted in any of the standard reference works on Irish writers, was praised by Yeats for its accurate and beautiful use of the half-Scottish dialect of the north. The story is unique in its portrayal of far darrigs as *giants* rather than diminutive beings.

"The Leprecaun; or Fairy Shoemaker," is typical of the poetry of William Allingham (1824-1889). Written by the customs officer who was the friend of several literary giants of his time, the poem first appeared in Allingham's *Irish Songs and Poems*.

The Crock of Gold, among James Stephens's most popular and enduring works, was first published in 1912 and confirms Frank O'Connor's description of the author as "a sort of literary acrobat, doing hair-raising swoops up in the roof of the tent." Aside from adding to our knowledge of the daily lives of leprechauns, the excerpt included in *The Leprechaun Book* reflects Stephens's humorous observations about the war between the sexes. The complete book should be read and enjoyed by every literate person.

"The Gollan," by A. E. Coppard (1873-1957), whose many short stories have been described as modern folk tales, is a thoroughly original treatment of the leprechaun. Far from basing the creature on elements from the conventional past, Coppard places the leprechaun within a context compellingly modern and astonishingly imaginative.

"The Fairy Shoe," by Edith Somerville (1858-1949), is a chapter from *The States Through Irish Eyes* (1931), the author's very amusing book about her travels in America in 1929. Almost everyone who is anyone in West Cork, and even those not so *au courant,* knows about the celebrated fairy shoe still in the possession of the author's family in the delightful village of Castletownshend. Those who have been privy to a view of the relic say that it is the very image of the author's drawing on page 103. Even sceptics admit that the wee brogue has to be seen to be believed!

Finally, an excerpt from the most famous leprechaun story of them all brings this anthology to a close. Herminie Kavanagh's Darby O'Gill is known to children throughout the world. His adventure with a leprechaun is only one of several encounters with Kavanagh's "good people," but it is vividly and wittily observed and described, a fitting illustration of the proper behavior of any self-respecting leprechaun.

The leprechaun has not fared well in the latter part of the twentieth century. Hawking breakfast cereal in television advertisements, and even portrayed recently as a psychopathic killer in one of the worst horror movies ever made, the leprechaun has been wildly misrepresented and maligned in our time. Perhaps *The Leprechaun Book* will help to set the record straight.

Lepracaun, Cluricaun, Far Darrig

W. B. Yeats

"THE NAME *Lepracaun*," Mr. Douglas Hyde writes to me, "is from the Irish *leith brog*—i.e., the One-shoemaker, since he is generally seen working at a single shoe. It is spelt in Irish *leith bhrogan*, or *leith phrogan,* and is in some places pronounced Luchryman, as O'Kearney writes it in that very rare book, the *Feis Tigh Chonain.*"

The *Lepracaun, Cluricaun*, and *Far Darrig*. Are these one spirit in different moods and shapes? Hardly two Irish writers are agreed. In many things these three fairies, if three, resemble each other. They are withered, old, and solitary, in every way unlike the sociable spirits. They dress with an unfairy homeliness, and are, indeed, most sluttish, slouching, jeering, mischievous phantoms. They are the great practical jokers among the good people.

The *Lepracaun* makes shoes continually, and has grown very rich. Many treasure-crocks, buried of old in wartime, has he now for his own. In the early part of this century, according to Croker, in a newspaper office in Tipperary, they used to show a little shoe forgotten by a Lepracaun.

The *Cluricaun* (*Clobhair-ceann* in O'Kearney) makes himself drunk in gentlemen's cellars. Some suppose he is merely the Lepracaun on a spree. He is almost unknown in Connaught and the north.

The *Far Darrig* (*fear dearg*), which means the Red Man, for he wears a red cap and coat, busies himself with practical joking, especially with gruesome joking. This he does, and nothing else.

The Leprechawn
D. R. McAnally, Jr.

EVERY MYTHOLOGY has its good and evil spirits which are objects of adoration and subjects of terror, and often both classes are worshipped from opposite motives; the good, that the worshipper may receive benefit; the evil, that he may escape harm. Sometimes good deities are so benevolent that they are neglected, superstitious fear directing all devotion towards the evil spirits to propitiate them and avert the calamities they are ever ready to bring upon the human race; sometimes the malevolent deities have so little power that the prayer of the pious is offered up to the good spirits that they may pour out still further favors, for man is a worshipping being, and will prostrate himself with equal fervor before the altar whether the deity be good or bad.

Midway, however, between the good and evil beings of all mythologies there is often one whose qualities are mixed; not wholly good nor entirely evil, but balanced between the two, sometimes doing a generous action, then descending to a petty meanness, but never rising to nobility of character nor sinking to the depths of depravity; good from whim, and mischievous from caprice.

Such a being is the Leprechawn of Ireland, a relic of the pagan mythology of that country. By birth the Leprechawn is of low descent, his father being an evil spirit and his mother a degenerate fairy; by nature he is a mischief-maker, the Puck of the Emerald Isle. He is of diminutive size, about three feet high, and is dressed in a little red jacket or roundabout, with red breeches buckled at the knee, gray or black stockings, and a hat, cocked in the style of a century ago, over a little, old, withered face. Round his neck is an Elizabethan ruff, and frills of lace are at his wrists. On the wild west coast, where the Atlantic winds bring almost constant rains, he dispenses with ruff and frills and wears a frieze overcoat over his pretty red suit, so that, unless on the lookout for the cocked hat, "ye might pass a Leprechawn on the road and never know it's himself that's in it at all."

In Clare and Galway, the favorite amusement of the Leprechawn is riding a sheep or goat, or even a dog, when the other animals are not available, and if the sheep look weary in the morning or the dog is muddy and worn out with fatigue, the peasant understands that the local Leprechawn has been going on some errand that lay at a greater distance than he cared to travel on foot. Aside from riding the sheep and dogs almost to death, the Leprechawn is credited with much small mischief about the house. Sometimes he will make the pot boil over and put out the fire, then again he will make it impossible for the pot to boil at all. He will steal the bacon-flitch, or empty the potato-kish, or fling the baby down on the floor, or occasionally will throw the few poor articles of furniture about the room with a strength and vigor altogether disproportioned to his diminutive size. But his mischievous pranks seldom go further than to drink up all the milk or despoil the proprietor's bottle of its poteen, sometimes, in sportiveness, filling the bottle with water, or, when very angry, leading the fire up to the thatch, and then startling the inmates of the cabin with his laugh as they rise, frightened, to put out the flames.

To offset these troublesome attributes, the Leprechawn is very domestic, and sometimes attaches himself to a family, always of the "rale owld shtock," accompanying its representatives from the castle to the cabin and never deserting them unless driven away by some act of insolence or negligence, "for, though he likes good atin', he wants what he gets to come wid an open hand, an' 'ud laver take the half av a pratee that's freely given than the whole av a quail that's begrudged him." But what he eats must be specially intended for him, an instance being cited by a Clare peasant of a Leprechawn that deserted an Irish family, because, on one occasion, the dog having left a portion of his food, it was set by for the Leprechawn. "Jakers, 'twas as mad as a little wasp he was, an' all that night they heard him workin' away in the cellar as busy as a nailer, an' a sound like a catheract av wather goin' widout saycin'. In the mornin' they wint to see what he'd been at, but he was gone, an' whin they come to thry for the wine, bad loock to the dhrop he'd left, but all was gone from ivery cask an' bottle, and they were filled wid say-wather, beways av rayvinge o' what they done him."

In different country districts the Leprechawn has different names. In the northern counties he is the Logheryman; in Tipperary, he is the Lurigadawne; in Kerry, the Luricawne; in Monaghan, the Cluricawne. The dress also varies. The Logheryman wears the uniform of some British infantry regiments, a red coat and white breeches, but instead of a cap, he wears a broad-brimmed, high, pointed hat, and after doing some trick more than usually mischievous, his favorite position is to poise himself on the extreme point of his hat, standing at the top of a wall or on a house, feet in the air, then laugh heartily and disappear. The Lurigadawne wears an antique slashed jacket of red, with peaks all round and a jockey cap, also sporting a sword, which he uses as a magic wand. The Luricawne is a fat, pursy little fellow whose jolly round face rivals in redness the cutaway jacket he wears, that always has seven rows of seven buttons in each row, though what use they are has never been determined, since his jacket is never buttoned, nor, indeed, can it be, but falls away from a shirt invariably white as the snow. When in full dress he wears a helmet several sizes too large for him, but, in general, prudently discards this article of headgear as having a tendency to render him conspicuous in a country where helmets are obsolete, and wraps his head in a handkerchief that he ties over his ears.

The Cluricawne of Monaghan is a little dandy, being gorgeously arrayed in a swallow-tailed evening coat of red with green vest, white breeches, black stockings, and shoes that "fur the shine av 'em 'ud shame a lookin'-glass." His hat is a long cone without a brim, and is usually set jauntily on one side of his curly head. When greatly provoked, he will sometimes take vengeance by suddenly ducking and poking the sharp point of his hat into the eye of the offender. Such conduct is, however, exceptional, as he commonly contents himself with soundly abusing those at whom he has taken offence, the objects of his anger hearing his voice but seeing nothing of his person.

One of the most marked peculiarities of the Leprechawn family is their intense hatred of schools and schoolmasters, arising, perhaps, from the ridicule of them by teachers, who affect to disbelieve in the existence of the Leprechawn and thus insult him, for "it's very well beknownst, that onless ye belave in him an' thrate him well, he'll lave an' come back no more." He does not even like to remain in the neighborhood where a national school has been established, and as such schools are now numerous in Ireland, the Leprechawns are becoming scarce. "Wan gineration of taichers is enough for thim, bekase the families where the little fellys live forgit to set thim out the bit an' sup, an' so they lave." The few that remain must have a hard time keeping soul and body together for nowhere do they now receive any attention at mealtimes, nor is the anxiety to see one by any means so great as in the childhood of men still living. Then, to catch a Leprechawn was certain fortune to him who had the wit to hold the mischief-maker a captive until demands for wealth were complied with.

"Mind ye," said a Kerry peasant, "the onliest time ye can ketch the little vagabone is whin he's settin' down, an' he niver sets down axceptin' whin his brogues want mendin'. He runs about so much he wears thim out, an' whin he feels his feet on the ground, down he sets undher a hidge or behind a wall, or in the grass, an' takes thim aff an' mends thim. Thin comes you by, as quiet as a cat an' sees him there, that ye can aisily, be his red coat, an' you shlippin' up on him, catches him in yer arrums.

"'Give up yer goold,' says you.

"'Begob, I've no goold,' says he.

"'Then outs wid yer magic purse,' says you.

"But it's like pullin' a hat full av taith to get aither purse or goold av him. He's got goold be the ton, an' can tell ye where ye can put yer finger on it, but he wont, till ye make him, an' that ye must do be no aisey manes. Some cuts aff his wind be chokin' him, an' some bates him, but don't for the life o' ye take yer eyes aff him, fur if ye do, he's aff like a flash an' the same man niver sees him agin, an' that's how it was wid Michael O'Dougherty.

"He was afther lookin' for wan night a year, fur he wanted to get married an' hadn't anny money, so he thought the aisiest was to ketch a Luricawne. So he was lookin' an' watchin' an' the fellys makin' fun av him all the time. Wan night he was comin' back afore day from a wake he'd been at, an' on the way home he laid undher the hidge an' shlept awhile, thin riz an' walked on. So as he was walkin', he seen a Luricawne in the grass be the road a-mendin' his brogues. So he shlipped up an' got him fast enough, an' thin made him tell him where was his goold. The Luricawne tuk him to nigh the place in the break o' the hills an' was goin' fur to show him, when all at wanst Mike heard the most outprobrious scraich over the head av him that 'ud make the hairs av ye shtand up like a mad cat's tail.

"'The saints defind me,' says he, 'what's that?' an' he looked up from the Luricawne that he was carryin' in his arrums. That minnit the little attomy wint out av his sight, fur he looked away from it an' it was gone, but he heard it laugh when it wint an' he niver got the goold but died poor, as me father knows, an' he a boy when it happened."

Although the Leprechawns are skilful in evading curious eyes, and, when taken, are shrewd in escaping from their captors, their tricks are sometimes all in vain, and after resorting to every device in their power, they are occasionally compelled to yield up their hidden stores, one instance of which was narrated by a Galway peasant.

"It was Paddy Donnelly av Connemara. He was always hard at work as far as anny wan seen, an' bad luck to the day he'd miss, barrin' Sundays. When all 'ud go to the fair, sorra a fut he'd shtir to go near it, no more did a dhrop av dhrink crass his lips. When they'd ax him why he didn't take divarshun, he'd laugh an' tell thim his field was divarshun enough fur him, an' by an' by he got rich, so they knewn that when they were at the fair or wakes or shports, it was lookin' fur a Leprechawn he was an' not workin', an' he got wan too, fur how else cud he get rich at all."

And so it must have been, in spite of the denials of Paddy Donnelly, though, to do him justice, he stoutly affirmed that his small property was acquired by industry, economy, and temperance. But according to the opinions of his neighbors, "bad scran to him 'twas as greedy as a pig he was, fur he knewn where the goold was, an' wanted it all fur himself, an' so lied about it like the Leprechawns, that's known to be the biggest liars in the world."

The Leprechawn is an old bachelor elf who successfully resists all efforts of scheming fairy mammas to marry him to young and beautiful fairies, persisting in single blessedness even in exile from his kind, being driven off as a punishment for his heterodoxy on matrimonial subjects. This is one explanation of the fact that Leprechawns are always seen alone, though other authorities make the Leprechawn solitary by preference, he having learned the hollowness of fairy friendship and the deceitfulness of fairy femininity, and left the society of his kind in disgust at its lack of sincerity.

It must be admitted that the latter explanation seems the more reasonable, since whenever the Leprechawn has been captured and forced to engage in conversation with his captor he displayed conversational powers that showed an ability to please, and as womankind, even among fairy circles, are, according to an Irish proverb, "aisily caught be an oily tongue," the presumption is against the expulsion of the Leprechawn and in favor of his voluntary retirement. However this may be, one thing is certain to the minds of all wise women and fairy-men, that he is the "thrickiest little divil that iver wore a brogue," whereof abundant proof is given. There was Tim O'Donovan, of Kerry, who captured a Leprechawn and forced him to disclose the spot where the "pot o' goold" was concealed. Tim was going to make the little rogue dig up the money for him, but, on the Leprechawn advancing the plea that he had no spade, released him, marking the spot by driving a stick into the ground and placing his hat on it. Returning the next morning with a spade, the spot pointed out by the "little ottomy av a desaver" being in the center of a large bog, he found, to his unutterable disgust, that the Leprechawn was too smart for him, for in every direction innumerable sticks rose out of the bog, each bearing aloft an old "caubeen" so closely resembling his own that poor

Tim, after long search, was forced to admit himself baffled and give up the gold that, on the evening before, had been fairly within his grasp, if "he'd only had the brains in his shkull to make the Leprechawn dig it for him, shpade or no shpade."

Even when caught, therefore, the captor must outwit the captive, and the wily little rascal, having a thousand devices, generally gets away without giving up a penny, and sometimes succeeds in bringing the eager fortune-hunter to grief, a notable instance of which was the case of Dennis O'Bryan, of Tipperary, as narrated by an old woman of Crusheen.

"It's well beknownst that the Leprechawn has a purse that's got the charmed shillin'. Only wan shillin', but the wondher av the purse is this: No matther how often ye take out a shillin' from it, the purse is niver empty at all, but whin ye put yer finger in agin, ye always find wan there, fur the purse fills up when ye take wan from it, so ye may shtand all day countin' out the shillin's an' they comin', that's a thrick av the good peoples an' be magic.

"Now Dinnis was a young blaggard that was always afther peepin' about undher the hidge fur to ketch a Leprechawn, though they do say that thim that doesn't sarch afther thim sees thim oftener than thim that does, but Dinnis made his mind up that if there was wan in the counthry, he'd have him fur he hated work worse than sin, an' did be settin' in a shebeen day in an' out till you'd think he'd grow on the sate. So wan day he was comin' home, an' he seen something red over in the corner o' the field, an' in he goes, as quiet as a mouse, an' up on the Leprechawn an' grips him be the collar an' downs him on the ground.

"'Arrah, now, ye ugly little vagabone,' says he, 'I've got ye at last. Now give up yer goold, or by jakers I'll choke the life out av yer pin-squazin' carkidge, ye owld cobbler, ye,' says he, shakin' him fit to make his head dhrop aff.

"The Leprechawn begged, and scritched, an' cried, an' said he wasn't a rale Leprechawn that was in it, but a young wan that hadn't anny goold, but Dinnis wouldn't let go av him, an' at last the Leprechawn said he'd take him to the pot ov goold that was hid be the say, in a glen in Clare. Dinnis didn't want to go so far, bein' afeared the Leprechawn 'ud get away, an' he thought the divilish baste was afther lyin' to him, bekase he knewn there was goold closter than that, an' so he was chokin' him that his eyes stood out till ye cud knock 'em aff wid a shtick, an' the Leprechawn axed him would he lave go if he'd give him the magic purse. Dinnis thought he'd betther do it, fur he was mortially afeared the oudacious little villin 'ud do him some thrick an' get away, so he tuk the purse, afther lookin' at it to make sure it was red shilk, an' had the shillin' in it, but the minnit he tuk his two eyes aff the Leprechawn, away wint the rogue wid a laugh that Dinnis didn't like at all.

"But he was feelin' very comfortable be razon av gettin' the purse, an' says to himself, 'Begorra, 'tis mesilf that'll ate the full av me waistband fur wan time, an' dhrink till a stame-ingine can't squaze wan dhrop more down me neck,' says he, and aff he goes like a quarther-horse fur Miss Clooney's sheebeen, that's where he used fur to go. In he goes, an' there was Paddy Grogan, an' Tim O'Donovan, an' Mike Conathey, an' Bryan Flaherty, an' a shtring more av 'em settin' on the table, an' he pulls up a sate an' down he sets, a callin' to Miss Clooney to bring her best.

"'Where's yer-money?' says she to him, fur he didn't use to have none barrin' a tuppence or so.

"'Do you have no fear,' says he, 'fur the money,' says he, 'ye pinny-schrapin' owld shkeleton,' this was beways av a shot at her, fur it was the size av a load o' hay she was, an' weighed a ton. 'Do you bring yer best,' says he. 'I'm a gintleman av forchune, bad loock to the job o' work I'll do till the life laves me. Come, jintlemin, drink at my axpinse.' An' so they did an' more than wanst, an' afther four or five guns apace, Dinnis ordhered dinner fur thim all, but Miss Clooney towld him sorra the bit or sup more 'ud crass the lips av him till he paid fur that he had. So out he pulls the magic purse fur to pay, an to show it thim an towld thim that it was an' where he got it.

"'And was it the Leprechawn gev it ye?' says they.

"It was,' says Dinnis, 'an' the varchew av this purse is sich, that if ye take shillins out av it be the handful all day long, they'll be comin' in a shtrame like whishkey out av a jug,' says he, pullin' out wan.

"And thin, me jewel, he put in his fingers afther another, but it wasn't there, for the Leprechawn made a ijit av him, an' instid o' givin' him the right purse, gev him wan just like it, so as onless ye looked clost, ye cudn't make out the differ betune thim. But the face on Dinnis was a holy show when he seen the Leprechawn had done him, an' he wid only a shillin', an' half a crown av dhrink down the troats av thim.

"'To the divil wid you an' yer Leprechawns, an' purses, an' magic shillins,' schreamed Miss Clooney, belavin', an' small blame to her that's, that it was lyin' to her he was. 'Ye're a thafe, so ye are, dhrinkin' up me dhrink, wid a lie on yer lips about the purse, and insultin' me into the bargain,' says she, thinkin' how he called her a shkeleton, an' her a load fur a waggin. 'Yer impidince bates owld Nick, so it does,' says she; so she up an' hits him a power av a crack on the head wid a bottle; an' the other felly's, a-thinkin' sure that it was a lie he was afther tellin' them, an' he laving thim to pay fur the dhrink he'd had, got on him an' belted him out av the face till it was nigh onto dead he was. Then a consthable comes along an' hears the phillaloo they did be makin' an' comes in.

"'Tatther an' agers,' says he, 'lave off. I command the pace. What's the matther here?'

"'Lave go,' says Dinnis, 'Sure what's the harrum o' getting the purse av a Leprechawn?'

"'None at all,' says the polisman, 'av ye projuice the Leprechawn an' make him teshtify he gev it ye an' that ye haven't been burglarious an' sarcumvinted another man's money,' says he.

"But Dinnis cudn't do it, so the cunsthable tumbled him into jail. From that he wint to coort an' got thirty days at hard labor, that he niver done in his life afore, an' afther he got out, he said he'd left lookin' for Leprechawns, fur they were too shmart fur him entirely, an' it's thrue for him, bekase I belave they were."

Leprechauns, Cluricauns, Far Darrigs

Carolyn White

THE LEPRECHAUN is a solitary creature avoiding contact not only with mortals but with other leprechauns, and, indeed, with the entire fairy tribe. He cannot endure their fickle frivolity nor they his dour manner. While trooping fairies delight in variegated experience, he pours all the passion of his concentrated soul into the careful making of shoes. A leprechaun will always be found with a shoe in one hand and a hammer in the other.

All leprechauns are ugly, stunted creatures, no taller than boys of ten or twelve, but broad and bulky, with faces like dried apples. But their eyes are always mischievously alight, and their bodies, despite their stubbiness, lithe. Leprechauns disappear behind trees faster than the mortal eye can follow.

And despite their possession of all the earth's treasure, they never sport clothes more elegant than drab, usually gray-colored coats, sturdy leather pocket-studded aprons and, for a bit of color, dusty-red cocked hats.

Leprechauns are a querulous, sottish and foul-mouthed breed—the bane of the fairer fairylanders. They smoke ill-smelling stumps of pipes called dudeens and guzzle intemperate draughts of beer from ever handy jugs. But the fairy gentry endure them because they provide the much needed service of cobblery. A few nights of intensive fairy dancing wear even the sturdiest of shoes; and so the leprechauns must ply their trade assiduously to meet the fairy demand. Luckily, drinking never unsteadies the hand holding the hammer.

Leprechauns guard the fairies' treasure as well as shoe their feet. Not only must they prevent the theft of treasure by mortals, but they must avert its waste by their profligate trooping brethren. Trooping fairies do not understand the value of a ruby nor care to store for the future. They are lavish when they have, indifferent when they have not. Without the leprechauns as bankers, the fairies would centuries ago have squandered their fortune within and without their borders. Since treasure belongs to all fairies, any fairy can spend, much to the leprechauns' chagrin, what he wills. And so although leprechauns grumble, they begrudgingly give what is asked; for, in truth, leprechauns live in awe of their fine-featured relatives.

Unlike the trooping fairies, the solitary fairies have a memory for the past. The trooping *sidhe* cannot keep abreast of short-lived mortal affairs; the solitary fairies never forget, but limit their interests. Whereas the banshees recall great mortal deeds, leprechauns (alone of the *sidhe*) remember when the marauding Danes landed in Ireland and where they hid their treasure. This memorable virtue, coupled with a remembrance of subsequent burials, gives leprechauns the decided advantage in treasure-guarding.

Although leprechauns bury their treasure well to keep it from profligate fairy and greedy mortal hands, rainbows frustrate their efforts by rudely settling themselves over particular gold hordes. By its presence a rainbow alerts mortals to a treasure's whereabouts, thereby causing the guardian-leprechaun incalculable anxiety. No matter how fast the little creature moves his pot, he never eludes the adherent rainbow. Luckily he usually manages to elude the grasp of the pursuant mortal, always baffled at the rainbow's inaccessibility.

If a mortal catches a leprechaun (a possible task due to his absorption in treasure-counting and his frequent overindulgence in drink), he must closely hold the little fellow, fixing an eye on him, and sternly demand his treasure. The leprechaun never refuses. But only a rare man actually recovers the horde. Invariably the leprechaun manages to turn the man's head— perhaps with a tale of his favorite horse's fall into the sinking bog and, like a greased pig, slips from the tight grip. Once a man forced a leprechaun to disclose a treasure buried beneath a tree. Tying a red scarf around the tree to mark it, the man then dashed home for a spade, having elicited from the leprechaun an oath to touch neither scarf nor treasure. And neither did he. But when the man returned, every tree in the wood sported a red scarf.

Since mortals and fairies either avoid them or approach them to exact their gold, leprechauns have become accustomed to trust only themselves. But kind acts sentimentally affect them and prompt them to respond in a generous manner. Sometimes in a moment of alcoholic geniality a leprechaun offers a mortal not only a drink but some of his treasure, or a shilling contained in a leather purse having the property of perpetual replenishment. An impoverished nobleman who had given a wee fellow a lift on his horse found his dilapidated castle the next day stacked to its leaky ceiling with gold coins. Once a leprechaun with a sentimental streak gave his treasure to a man claiming part-leprechaun blood. And on an extraordinarily generous occasion one gave a golden bridle which, whenever shaken, produced a strong yellow steed attached to it.

Female leprechauns do not exist; and since female fairies and mortals find the males physically repulsive, leprechaun-reproduction is doubtful. Leprechauns themselves are reticent about their births as they are secretive about most things. Perhaps they were the defective children of beautiful fairy parents who ejected them from the fairy troop because of their shape and disposition, but endured their separated existences as long as they cobbled shoes and guarded treasure.

Much debate has arisen as to whether cluricauns are actually leprechauns or degenerate close cousins. Save for a pink tinge about the nose, cluricauns perfectly resemble leprechauns in all their physical construction. But they never sport an apron or carry a hammer or manifest any desire to work. They look and act like weekend gentlemen: silver buckles adorn their shoes, gold laces their caps, and pale blue stockings their stocky calves. They unabashedly enter rich men's wine cellars as if they were their own and drain the casks. For amusement they harness sheep and goats and shepherds' dogs, jump the bogs, and race them over the fields through the night until the beasts are muddy and beaten with fatigue.

Leprechauns sternly declare these pleasure-seekers to be none of their own. Those believing their word argue that while extravagantly clothed cluricauns tipple the wine glass, self-respecting leprechauns in working dress drink nothing but beer. Yet since cluricauns do act like working men putting on aristocratic airs, many suspect them to be nothing other than leprechauns on a spree, who, in the sobering morning, haughtily deny a perverse double nature. The question remains insoluble because neither reckless drunkards nor creatures with reputations to preserve can be thoroughly trusted.

The far darrig (or fear dearg) is a near relation to the leprechaun, with similar puckered features and a short stocky body. His face is splotched as yellow as buttermilk clots; he dresses in red from his sugar-loaf hat to his tail-trailing cape to the woolen stockings which cling to his calves. Hence his name—the far darrig or red man. He is reputed not only for his color (for he sometimes travels invisibly) but for his delight in all varieties of mischief and mockery, especially in gruesome practical joking. He manipulates his voice most wondrously, emitting sounds like the thudding of waves on rocks or the cooing of pigeons; his forte is the dull, hollow laugh of a dead man from within a vast and rain-sodden tomb.

Mortal terror amuses the far darrig. On occasion he invites a mortal to enter a lonely bog hut, whereupon he orders him to make dinner out of a naked hag skewered on a spit. The man invariably faints. When he recovers, he finds himself alone and chilled on the bog with the sound of derisive laughter swelling the air, but coming from no distinguishable source. It is advisable to say *"Na déan magadh fúm"* — "do not mock me" — upon encountering a far darrig, lest one be caught fast in some macabre game. Unfortunately, he plans his tricks so cleverly that a mortal is snared long before he realizes the need to protest. Preventive measures, at that point, no longer apply.

Ironically, with all his pranks, the far darrig desires not to do harm but to show favor. He is actually a good-natured sort, bringing luck to those whom he approves; but he cannot resist a preliminary teasing. A notorious far darrig named Teigue constantly frequented a certain house; the room echoed with his unearthly laughter, but he never injured the inhabitants or their guests. Teigue instinctively knew each one's secrets and accomplishments; and he had a particular fondness for music. If any had musical talents which they were too modest to profess, he never politely requested a performance, but methodically terrorized them into admitting their ability and giving a tune.

Whenever Teigue entered the house, he cordially greeted the master and requested his usual glass of whiskey. A far darrig likes his comfort, and assumes that mortals are conveniently placed on earth to administer to it. A comfortable hearth in winter, a good shot of poteen, and a filled pipe by the sofa are the minimum requirements. And if the house is clean and well-regulated the red man so works his fairy will that equanimity sustains itself and the household prospers.

A certain far darrig entered the house of his choice each evening promptly at eleven o'clock. He expected fire, pipe, and whiskey in their respective places and the inhabitants safe in bed. Each night he stuck his hairy little arm through the keyhole, opened the door, and made himself at home. Fearing his vengeance (for, if crossed, he was likely to destroy them or their cattle), the family acceded to his eccentricities and so became rich and remained healthy. Yet when they moved he refused to go, but awaited the accustomed service from the new tenants. Evidently, red men attach themselves to houses and not families.

Although the far darrig enjoys his comfort; he likes a modicum of adventure. Whenever fairies of foreign parts attack his lands, he quits his solitary comfort, jumps on a well-groomed steed and effectively commands the native fairy forces. If mortals inadvertently cross his path, he saddles and bridles them and converts them into war-horses for the battle's duration. Such happened to Diarmuid Bawn, the piper, who became a lead-charger for the victorious faction and was consequently rewarded with a lifetime supply of tobacco for the midnight service.

Some claim that the red men are humans who return from the dead either because they found Heaven or Hell excessive or the mortal life-style eternally satisfactory. But red men are, in truth, fairy men who, never quite adjusting to manic fairy habits, have always harbored a sentimental affection for the more subdued manners of humankind.

The Field of Boliauns
Joseph Jacobs

ONE FINE DAY in harvest—it was indeed Ladyday in harvest, that everybody knows to be one of the greatest holidays in the year—Tom Fitzpatrick was taking a ramble through the ground, and went along the sunny side of a hedge; when all of a sudden he heard a clacking sort of noise a little before him in the hedge. "Dear me," said Tom, "but isn't it surprising to hear the stonechatters singing so late in the season?" So Tom stole on, going on the tops of his toes to try if he could get a sight of what was making the noise, to see if he was right in his guess. The noise stopped; but as Tom looked sharply through the bushes, what should he see in a nook of the hedge but a brown pitcher, that might hold about a gallon and a half of liquor; and by-and-by a little wee teeny tiny bit of an old man, with a little *motty* of a cocked hat stuck upon the top of his head, a deeshy daushy leather apron hanging before him, pulled out a little wooden stool, and stood up upon it, and dipped a little piggin into the pitcher, and took out the full of it, and put it beside the stool, and then sat down under the pitcher, and began to work at putting a heel-piece on a bit of a brogue just fit for himself. "Well, by the powers," said Tom to himself, "I often heard tell of the Lepracauns, and, to tell God's truth, I never rightly believed in them—but here's one of them in real earnest. If I go knowingly to work, I'm a made man. They say a body must never take their eyes off them, or they'll escape."

Tom now stole on a little further, with his eye fixed on the little man just as a cat does with a mouse. So when he got up quite close to him, "God bless your work, neighbor," said Tom.

The little man raised up his head, and "Thank you kindly,"

said he.

"I wonder you'd be working on the holiday!" said Tom.

"That's my own business, not yours," was the reply.

"Well, maybe you'd be civil enough to tell us what you've got in the pitcher there?" said Tom.

"That I will with pleasure," said he; "it's good beer."

"Beer!" said Tom. "Thunder and fire! where did you get it?"

"Where did I get it, is it? Why, I made it. And what do you think I made it of?"

"Devil a one of me knows," said Tom; "but of malt, I suppose, what else?"

"There you're out. I made it of heath."

"Of heath!" said Tom, bursting out laughing; "sure you don't think me to be such a fool as to believe that?"

"Do as you please," said he, "but what I tell you is the truth. Did you never hear tell of the Danes?"

"Well, what about them?" said Tom.

"Why, when they were here they taught us to make beer out of the heath, and the secret's in my family ever since."

"Will you give a body a taste of your beer?" said Tom.

"I'll tell you what it is, young man, it would be fitter for you to be looking after your father's property than to be bothering decent quiet people with your foolish questions. There now, while you're idling away your time here, there's the cows have broke into the oats, and are knocking the corn all about."

Tom was taken so by surprise with this that he was just on the very point of turning round when he recollected himself; so, afraid that the like might happen again, he made a grab at the Lepracaun, and caught him up in his hand; but in his hurry he overset the pitcher, and spilled all the beer, so that he could not get a taste of it to tell what sort it was. He then swore that he would kill him if he did not show him where his money was.

Tom looked so wicked and so bloody-minded that the little man was quite frightened; so says he, "Come along with me a couple of fields off, and I'll show you a crock of gold."

So they went, and Tom held the Lepracaun fast in his hand, and never took his eyes from off him, though they had to cross hedges and ditches, and a crooked bit of bog, till at last they came to a great field all full of boliauns, and the Lepracaun pointed to a big boliaun, and says he, "Dig under that boliaun, and you'll get the great crock all full of guineas."

Tom in his hurry had never thought of bringing a spade with him, so he made up his mind to run home and fetch one; and that he might know the place again he took off one of his red garters, and tied it round the boliaun.

Then he said to the Lepracaun, "Swear ye'll not take that garter away from that boliaun." And the Lepracaun swore right away not to touch it.

"I suppose," said the Lepracaun, very civilly, "you have no further occasion for me?"

"No," says Tom; "you may go away now, if you please, and God speed you, and may good luck attend you wherever you go."

"Well, good-bye to you, Tom Fitzpatrick," said the Lepracaun; "and much good might it do you when you get it."

So Tom ran for dear life, till he came home and got a spade, and then away with him, as hard as he could go, back to the field of boliauns; but when he got there, lo and behold! not a boliaun in the field but had a red garter, the very model of his own, tied about it; and as to digging up the whole field, that was all nonsense, for there were more than forty good Irish acres in it. So Tom came home again with his spade on his shoulder, a little cooler than he went, and many's the hearty curse he gave the Lepracaun every time he thought of the neat turn he had served him.

Master and Man
Thomas Crofton Croker

BILLY MAC DANIEL was once as likely a young man as ever shook his brogue at a patron,* emptied a quart or handled a shillelagh; fearing for nothing but the want of drink; caring for nothing but who should pay for it; and thinking of nothing but how to make fun over it; drunk or sober, a word and a blow was ever the way with Billy Mac Daniel; and a mighty easy way it is of either getting into or of ending a dispute. More is the pity that, through the means of his thinking, and fearing, and caring for nothing, this same Billy Mac Daniel fell into bad company; for surely the good people are the worst of all company anyone could come across.

It so happened that Billy was going home one clear frosty night not long after Christmas; the moon was round and bright; but although it was as fine a night as heart could wish for, he felt pinched with cold. "By my word," chattered Billy, "a drop of good liquor would be no bad thing to keep a man's soul from freezing in him; and I wish I had a full measure of the best."

"Never wish it twice, Billy," said a little man in a three-cornered hat, bound all about with gold lace, and with great silver buckles in his shoes, so big that it a wonder how he could carry them, and he held out a glass as big as himself, filled with as good liquor as eye ever looked on or lip tasted.

"Success, my little fellow," said Billy Mac Daniel nothing daunted, though well he knew the little man to belong to the *good people*; "here's your health, anyway, and thank you kindly; no matter who pays for the drink"; and he took the glass and drained it to the very bottom without ever taking a second

---

* A festival held in honor of some patron saint.

breath to it.

"Success," said the little man; "and you're heartily welcome, Billy; but don't think to cheat me as you have done others—out with your purse and pay me like a gentleman."

"Is it I pay you?" said Billy; "could I not just take you up and put you in my pocket as easily as a blackberry?"

"Billy Mac Daniel," said the little man, getting very angry, "you shall be my servant for seven years and a day, and that is the way I will be paid; so make ready to follow me."

When Billy heard this he began to be very sorry for having used such bold words toward the little man; and he felt himself, yet could not tell how, obliged to follow the little man the live-long night about the country, up and down, and over hedge and ditch, and through bog and brake, without any rest.

When morning began to dawn the little man turned round to him and said, "You may now go home, Billy, but on your peril don't fail to meet me in the Fort-field tonight; or if you do it may be the worse for you in the long run. If I find you a good servant, you will find me an indulgent master."

Home went Billy Mac Daniel; and though he was tired and weary enough, never a wink of sleep could he get for thinking of the little man; but he was afraid not to do his bidding, so up he got in the evening, and away he went to the Fort-field. He was not long there before the little man came towards him and said, "Billy, I want to go a long journey tonight; so saddle one of my horses, and you may saddle another for yourself, as you are to go along with me, and may be tired after your walk last night."

Billy thought this very considerate of his master, and thanked him accordingly: "But," said he, "if I may be so bold, sir, I would ask which is the way to your stable, for never a thing do I see but the fort here, and the old thorn tree in the corner of the

field, and the stream running at the bottom of the hill, with the bit of bog over against us."

"Ask no questions, Billy," said the little man, "but go over to that bit of bog, and bring me two of the strongest rushes you can find."

Billy did accordingly, wondering what the little man would be at; and he picked two of the stoutest rushes he could find, with a little bunch of brown blossom stuck at the side of each, and brought them back to his master.

"Get up, Billy," said the little man, taking one of the rushes from him and striding across it.

"Where shall I get up, please your honor?" said Billy.

"Why, upon horseback, like me, to be sure," said the little man.

"Is it after making a fool of me you'd be," said Billy, "bidding me get a horseback upon that bit of a rush? Maybe you want to persuade me that the rush I pulled but a while ago out of the bog over there is a horse?"

"Up! up! and no words," said the little man, looking very angry; "the best horse you ever rode was but a fool to it." So Billy, thinking all this was in joke, and fearing to vex his master, straddled across the rush. "Borram! Borram! Borram!" cried the little man three times (which, in English, means to become great), and Billy did the same after him; presently the rushes swelled up into fine horses, and away they went full speed; but Billy, who had put the rush between his legs, without much minding how he did it, found himself sitting on horseback the wrong way, which was rather awkward, with his face to the horse's tail; and so quickly had his steed started off with him that he had no power to turn round, and there was therefore nothing for it but to hold on by the tail.

At last they came to their journey's end, and stopped at the gate of a fine house. "Now, Billy," said the little man, "do as you see me do, and follow me close; but as you did not know your horse's head from his tail, mind that your own head does not spin round until you can't tell whether you are standing on it or your heels; for remember that old liquor, though able to make a cat speak, can make a man dumb."

The little man then said some queer kind of words, out of which Billy could make no meaning; but he contrived to say them after him for all that; and in they both went through the keyhole of the door, and through one keyhole after another, until they got into the wine-cellar, which was well stored with all kinds of wine.

The little man fell to drinking as hard as he could, and Billy noway disliking the example, did the same. "The best of masters are you, surely," said Billy to him; "no matter who is the next; and well pleased will I be with your service if you continue to give me plenty to drink."

"I have made no bargain with you," said the little man, "and will make none; but up and follow me." Away they went, through keyhole after keyhole; and each mounting upon the rush which he left at the hall door, scampered off, kicking the clouds before them like snowballs, as soon as the words, "Borram, Borram, Borram," had passed their lips.

When they came back to the Fort-field the little man dismissed Billy, bidding him to be there the next night at the same hour. Thus did they go on, night after night, shaping their course one night here, and another night there; sometimes north, and sometimes east, and sometimes south, until there was not a gentleman's wine-cellar in all Ireland they had not visited, and could tell the flavor of every wine in it as well, ay, better than the butler himself.

One night when Billy Mac Daniel met the little man as usual

in the Fort-field, and was going to the bog to fetch the horses for their journey, his master said to him, "Billy, I shall want another horse tonight, for maybe we may bring back more company than we take." So Billy, who now knew better than to question any order given to him by his master, brought a third rush, much wondering who it might be that would travel back in their company, and whether he was about to have a fellow-servant. "If I have," thought Billy, "he shall go and fetch the horses from the bog every night; for I don't see why I am not, every inch of me, as good a gentleman as my master."

Well, away they went, Billy leading the third horse, and never stopped until they came to a snug farmer's house, in the county Limerick, close under the old castle of Carrigogunniel, that was built, they say, by the great Brian Boru. Within the house there was great carousing going forward, and the little man stopped outside for some time to listen; then turning round all of a sudden, said, "Billy, I will be a thousand years old tomorrow!"

"God bless us, sir," said Billy; "will you?"

"Don't say these words again, Billy," said the little old man, "or you will be my ruin forever. Now Billy, as I will be a thousand years in the world tomorrow, I think it is full time for me to get married."

"I think so too, without any kind of doubt at all," said Billy, "if ever you mean to marry."

"And to that purpose," said the little man, "have I come all the way to Carrigogunniel; for in this house, this very night, is young Darby Riley going to be married to Bridget Rooney; and as she is a tall and comely girl, and has come of decent people, I think of marrying her myself, and taking her off with me."

"And what will Darby Riley say to that?" said Billy.

"Silence" said the little man, putting on a mighty severe look; "I did not bring you here with me to ask questions," and without holding further argument, he began saying the queer words which had the power of passing him through the keyhole as free as air, and which Billy thought himself mighty clever to be able to say after him.

In they both went; and for the better viewing the company, the little man perched himself up as nimbly as a cocksparrow upon one of the big beams which went across the house over all their heads, and Billy did the same upon another facing him; but not being much accustomed to roosting in such a place, his legs hung down as untidy as may be, and it was quite clear he had not taken pattern after the way in which the little man had bundled himself up together. If the little man had been a tailor all his life, he could not have sat more contentedly upon his haunches.

There they were, both master and man, looking down upon the fun that was going forward; and under them were the priest and piper, and the father of Darby Riley, with Darby's two brothers and his uncle's son; and there were both the father and the mother of Bridget Rooney, and proud enough the old couple were that night of their daughter, as good right they had; and her four sisters, with brand-new ribbons in their caps, and her three brothers all looking as clean and as clever as any three boys in Munster, and there were uncles and aunts, and gossips and cousins enough besides to make a full house of it; and plenty was there to eat and drink on the table for everyone of them, if they had been double the number.

Now it happened, just as Mrs. Rooney had helped his reverence to the first cut of the pig's head which was placed before her, beautifully bolstered up with white savoys, that the bride gave a sneeze, which made everyone at the table start, but not a soul said "and bless us." All thinking that the priest would have done so, as he ought if he had done his duty, no one wished to take the word out of his mouth, which, unfortunately, was preoccupied with pig's head and greens. And after a moment's pause the fun and merriment of the bridal feast went on without the pious benediction.

Of this circumstance both Billy and his master were no inattentive spectators from their exalted stations. "Ha!" exclaimed the little man, throwing one leg from under him with a joyous flourish, and his eye twinkled with a strange light, while his eyebrows became elevated into the curvature of Gothic arches; "Ha!" said he, leering down at the bride, and then up at Billy, "I have half of her now, surely. Let her sneeze but twice more, and she is mine, in spite of priest, mass-book, and Darby Riley."

Again the fair Bridget sneezed; but it was so gently, and she blushed so much, that few except the little man took, or seemed to take, any notice; and no one thought of saying "God bless us."

Billy all this time regarded the poor girl with a most rueful expression of countenance; for he could not help thinking what a terrible thing it was for a nice young girl of nineteen, with large blue eyes, transparent skin, and dimpled cheeks, suffused with health and joy, to be obliged to marry an ugly little bit of a man, who was a thousand years old, barring a day.

At this critical moment the bride gave a third sneeze, and Billy roared out with all his might, "God save us!" Whether this exclamation resulted from his soliloquy, or from the mere force of habit, he never could tell exactly himself; but no sooner was it uttered than the little man, his face glowing with rage and disappointment, sprung from the beam on which he had perched himself, and shrieking out in the shrill voice of a cracked bagpipe, "I discharge you from my service, Billy Mac Daniel— take *that* for your wages," gave poor Billy a most furious kick in the back, which sent his unfortunate servant sprawling upon his face and hands right in the middle of the supper table.

If Billy was astonished, how much more so was everyone of the company into which he was thrown with so little ceremony. But when they heard his story, Father Cooney laid down his knife and fork, and married the young couple out of hand with all speed; and Billy Mac Daniel danced the Rinka at their wedding, and plenty he did drink at it too, which was what he thought more of than dancing.

Teig O'Kane and the Corpse

Douglas Hyde

THERE WAS ONCE a grown-up lad in the County Leitrim, and he was strong and lively, and the son of a rich farmer. His father had plenty of money, and he did not spare it on the son. Accordingly, when the boy grew up he liked sport better than work, and, as his father had no other children, he loved this one so much that he allowed him to do in everything just as it pleased himself. He was very extravagant, and he used to scatter the gold money as another person would scatter the white. He was seldom to be found at home, but if there was a fair, or a race, or a gathering within ten miles of him, you were dead certain to find him there. And he seldom spent a night in his father's house, but he used to be always out rambling, and, like Shawn Bwee long ago, there was

"grádh gach cailin i mbrollach a léine,"

"the love of every girl in the breast of his shirt," and it's many's the kiss he got and he gave, for he was very handsome, and there wasn't a girl in the country but would fall in love with him, only for him to fasten his two eyes on her, and it was for that someone made this *rann* on him—

"Look at the rogue, it's for kisses he's rambling,
    It isn't much wonder, for that was his way;
He's like an old hedgehog, at night he'll be scrambling
    From this place to that, but he'll sleep in the day."

At last he became very wild and unruly. He wasn't to be seen day or night in his father's house, but always rambling or going on his *kailee* (night visit) from place to place and from house to house, so that the old people used to shake their heads and say to one another, "It's easy seen what will happen to the land when the old man dies; his son will run through it in a year, and it won't stand him that long itself."

He used to be always gambling and card-playing and drinking, but his father never minded his bad habits, and never punished him. But it happened one day that the old man was told that the son had ruined the character of a girl in the neighborhood, and he was greatly angry, and he called the son to him, and said to him, quietly and sensibly—"Avic," says he, "you know I loved you greatly up to this, and I never stopped you from doing your choice thing whatever it was, and I kept plenty of money with you, and I always hoped to leave you the house and land, and all I had after myself would be gone; but I heard a story of you today that has disgusted me with you. I cannot tell you the grief that I felt when I heard such a thing of you, and I tell you now plainly that unless you marry that girl I'll leave house and land and everything to my brother's son. I never could leave it to anyone who would make so bad a use of it as you do yourself, deceiving women and coaxing girls. Settle with yourself now whether you'll marry that girl and get my land as a fortune with her, or refuse to marry her and give up all that was coming to you; and tell me in the morning which of the two things you have chosen."

"Och! *Domnoo Sheery*! father, you wouldn't say that to me, and I such a good son as I am. Who told you I wouldn't marry the girl?" says he.

But his father was gone, and the lad knew well enough that he would keep his word too; and he was greatly troubled in his mind, for as quiet and as kind as the father was, he never went back on a word that he had once said, and there wasn't another man in the country who was harder to bend than he was.

The boy did not know rightly what to do. He was in love with the girl indeed, and he hoped to marry her sometime or other, but he would much sooner have remained another while as he was, and follow on at his old tricks—drinking, sporting, and playing cards; and, along with that, he was angry that his father should order him to marry, and should threaten him if he did not do it.

"Isn't my father a great fool," says he to himself. "I was ready enough, and only too anxious, to marry Mary; and now since he threatened me, faith I've a great mind to let it go another while."

His mind was so much excited that he remained between two notions as to what he should do. He walked out into the night at last to cool his heated blood, and went on to the road. He lit a pipe, and as the night was fine he walked and walked on, until the quick pace made him begin to forget his trouble. The night was bright, and the moon half full. There was not a breath of wind blowing, and the air was calm and mild. He walked on for nearly three hours, when he suddenly remembered that it was late in the night, and time for him to turn. "Musha! I think I forgot myself," says he; "it must be near twelve o'clock now."

The word was hardly out of his mouth, when he heard the sound of many voices, and the trampling of feet on the road before him. "I don't know who can be out so late at night as this, and on such a lonely road," said he to himself.

He stood listening, and he heard the voices of many people talking, but he could not understand what they were saying. "Oh, wirra!" says he, "I'm afraid. It's not Irish or English they have; it can't be they're Frenchmen!" He went on a couple of yards further, and he saw well enough by the light of the moon a band of little people coming towards him, and they were carrying something big and heavy with them. "Oh, murder!" says he to himself, "sure it can't be that they're the good people that's in it!" Every *rib* of hair that was on his head stood up, and there fell a shaking on his bones, for he saw that they were coming to him fast.

He looked at them again, and perceived that there were about twenty little men in it, and there was not a man at all of them higher than about three feet or three feet and a half, and some of them were gray, and seemed very old. He looked again, but he could not make out what was the heavy thing they were carrying until they came up to him, and then they all stood round about him. They threw the heavy thing down on the road, and he saw on the spot that it was a dead body.

He became as cold as the Death, and there was not a drop of blood running in his veins when an old little gray *maneen* came up to him and said, "Isn't it lucky we met you, Teig O'Kane?"

Poor Teig could not bring out a word at all, nor open his lips, if he were to get the world for it, and so he gave no answer.

"Teig O'Kane," said the little gray man again, "isn't it timely you met us?"

Teig could not answer him.

"Teig O'Kane," says he, "the third time, isn't it lucky and timely that we met you?"

But Teig remained silent, for he was afraid to return an answer, and his tongue was as if it was tied to the roof of his mouth.

The little gray man turned to his companions, and there was joy in his bright little eye. "And now," says he, "Teig O'Kane hasn't a word, we can do with him what we please. Teig, Teig,'" says he, "you're living a bad life, and we can make a slave of you now, and you cannot withstand us, for there's no use in trying to go against us. Lift that corpse."

Teig was so frightened that he was only able to utter the two words, "I won't"; for as frightened as he was he was obstinate and stiff, the same as ever.

"Teig O'Kane won't lift the corpse," said the little *maneen* with a wicked little laugh, for all the world like the breaking of a *lock* of dry *kippeens*, and with a little harsh voice like the striking of a cracked bell. "Teig O'Kane won't lift the corpse— make him lift it"; and before the word was out of his mouth they had all gathered round poor Teig, and they all talking and laughing through each other.

Teig tried to run from them, but they followed him, and a man of them stretched out his foot before him as he ran, so that Teig was thrown in a heap on the road. Then before he could rise up the fairies caught him, some by the hands and some by the feet, and they held him tight, in a way that he could not stir, with his face against the ground. Six or seven of them raised the body then, and pulled it over to him, and left it down on his back. The breast of the corpse was squeezed against Teig's back and shoulders, and the arms of the corpse were thrown around Teig's neck. Then they stood back from him a couple of yards, and let him get up. He rose, foaming at the mouth and cursing, and he shook himself, thinking to throw the corpse off his back. But his fear and his wonder were great when he found that the two arms had a tight hold round his own neck, and that the two legs were squeezing his hips firmly, and that, however strongly he tried, he could not throw it off, any more than a horse can throw off its saddle. He was terribly frightened then, and he thought he was lost. "Ochone! for ever," said he to himself, "it's the bad life I'm leading that has given the good people this power over me. I promise to God and Mary, Peter and Paul, Patrick and Bridget, that I'll mend my ways for as long as I have to live, if I come clear out of this danger—and I'll marry the girl."

The little gray man came up to him again, and said he to him, "Now, Teig*een*," says he, "you didn't lift the body when I told you to lift it, and see how you were made to lift it; perhaps when I tell you to bury it, you won't bury it until you're made to bury it!"

"Anything at all that I can do for your honor," said Teig, "I'll do it," for he was getting sense already, and if it had not been for the great fear that was on him, he never would have let that civil word slip out of his mouth.

The little man laughed a sort of laugh again. "You're getting quiet now, Teig," says he. "I'll go bail but you'll be quiet enough before I'm done with you. Listen to me now, Teig O'Kane, and if you don't obey me in all I'm telling you to do, you'll repent it. You must carry with you this corpse that is on your back to Teampoll-Démus, and you must bring it into the church with you, and make a grave for it in the very middle of the church, and you must raise up the flags and put them down again the very same way, and you must carry the clay out of the church and leave the place as it was when you came, so that no one could know that there had been anything changed. But that's not all. Maybe that the body won't be allowed to be buried in that church; perhaps some other man has the bed, and, if so, it's likely he won't share it with this one. If you don't get leave to bury it in Teampoll-Démus, you must carry it to Carrick-fhad-vic-Orus, and bury it in the churchyard there; and if you don't get it into that place, take it with you to Teampoll-Ronan; and if that churchyard is closed on you, take it to Imlogue-Fada; and if you're not able to bury it there, you've no more to do than to take it to Kill-Breedya, and you can bury it there without hindrance. I cannot tell you what one of those churches is the one where you will have leave to bury that corpse under the clay, but I know that it will be allowed you to bury him at some church or other of them. If you do this work rightly, we will be thankful to you, and you will have no cause to grieve; but if you are slow or lazy, believe me we shall take satisfaction of you."

When the gray little man had done speaking, his comrades laughed and clapped their hands together. "Glic! Glic! Hwee! Hwee!" they all cried; "go on, go on, you have eight hours before you till daybreak, and if you haven't this man buried before the sun rises, you're lost." They struck a fist and a foot behind on him, and drove him on in the road. He was obliged to walk, and to walk fast, for they gave him no rest.

He thought himself that there was not a wet path, or a dirty *boreen*, or a crooked contrary road in the whole county, that he had not walked that night. The night was at times very dark, and whenever there would come a cloud across the moon he could see nothing, and then he used often to fall. Sometimes he was hurt, and sometimes he escaped, but he was obliged always to rise on the moment and to hurry on. Sometimes the moon would break out clearly, and then he would look behind him and see the little people following at his back. And he heard them speaking amongst themselves, talking and crying out, and screaming like a flock of seagulls; and if he was to save his soul he never understood as much as one word of what they were saying.

He did not know how far he had walked, when at last one of them cried out to him, "Stop here!" He stood, and they all gathered round him.

"Do you see those withered trees over there?" says the old boy to him again. "Teampoll-Démus is among those trees, and you must go in there by yourself, for we cannot follow you or go with you. We must remain here. Go on boldly."

Teig looked from him, and he saw a high wall that was in places half broken down, and an old gray church on the inside of the wall, and about a dozen withered old trees scattered here and there round it. There was neither leaf nor twig on any of them, but their bare crooked branches were stretched out like the arms of an angry man when he threatens. He had no help for it, but was obliged to go forward. He was a couple of hundred yards from the church, but he walked on, and never looked behind him until he came to the gate of the churchyard. The old gate was thrown down, and he had no difficulty in entering. He turned then to see if any of the little people were following him, but there came a cloud over the moon, and the night became so dark that he could see nothing. He went into the churchyard, and he walked up the old grassy pathway leading to the church. When he reached the door, he found it locked. The door was large and strong, and he did not know what to do. At last he drew out his knife with difficulty, and stuck it in the wood to try if it were not rotten, but it was not.

"Now," said he to himself, "I have no more to do; the door is shut, and I can't open it."

Before the words were rightly shaped in his own mind, a voice in his ear said to him, "Search for the key on the top of the door, or on the wall."

He started. "Who is that speaking to me?" he cried, turning round; but he saw no one. The voice said in his ear again, "Search for the key on the top of the door, or on the wall."

"What's that?" said he, and the sweat running from his forehead; "who spoke to me?"

"It's I, the corpse, that spoke to you!" said the voice.

"Can you talk?" said Teig.

"Now and again," said the corpse.

Teig searched for the key, and he found it on the top of the wall. He was too much frightened to say any more, but he opened the door wide, and as quickly as he could, and he went in, with the corpse on his back. It was as dark as pitch inside, and poor Teig began to shake and tremble.

"Light the candle," said the corpse.

Teig put his hand in his pocket, as well as he was able, and drew out a flint and steel. He struck a spark out of it, and lit a burnt rag he had in his pocket. He blew it until it made a flame, and he looked round him. The church was very ancient, and part of the wall was broken down. The windows were blown in or cracked, and the timbers of the seats were rotten. There were six or seven old iron candlesticks left there still, and in one of these candlesticks Teig found the stump of an old candle, and he lit it. He was still looking round him in the strange and horrid place in which he found himself, when the cold corpse whispered in his ear, "Bury me now, bury me now; there is a spade and turn the ground." Teig looked from him, and he saw a spade lying beside the altar. He took it up, and he placed the blade under a flag that was in the middle of the aisle, and leaning all his weight on the handle of the spade, he raised it. When the first flag was raised it was not hard to raise the others near it, and he moved three or four of them out of their places. The clay that was under them was soft and easy to dig, but he had not thrown up more than three or four shovelfuls when he felt the iron touch something soft like flesh. He threw up three or four more shovelfuls from around it, and then he saw that it was another body that was buried in the same place.

"I am afraid I'll never be allowed to bury the two bodies in the same hole," said Teig, in his own mind. "You corpse, there on my back," says he, "will you be satisfied if I bury you down here?" But the corpse never answered him a word.

"That's a good sign," said Teig to himself. "Maybe he's getting quiet," and he thrust the spade down in the earth again. Perhaps he hurt the flesh of the other body, for the dead man that was buried there stood up in the grave, and shouted an

awful shout. "Hoo! hoo!! hoo!!! Go! go!! go!!! or you're a dead, dead, dead man!" And then he fell back in the grave again. Teig said afterwards, that of all the wonderful things he saw that night, that was the most awful to him. His hair stood upright on his head like the bristles of a pig, the cold sweat ran off his face, and then came a tremor over all his bones, until he thought that he must fall.

But after a while he became bolder, when he saw that the second corpse remained lying quietly there, and he threw in the clay on it again, and he smoothed it overhead, and he laid down the flags carefully as they had been before. "It can't be that he'll rise up any more," said he.

He went down the aisle a little further, and drew near to the door, and began raising the flags again, looking for another bed for the corpse on his back. He took up three or four flags and put them aside, and then he dug the clay. He was not long digging until he laid bare an old woman without a thread upon her but her shirt. She was more lively than the first corpse, for he had scarcely taken any of the clay away from about her, when she sat up and began to cry, "Ho, you *bodach* (clown)! Ha, you *bodach*! Where has he been that he got no bed?"

Poor Teig drew back, and when she found that she was getting no answer, she closed her eyes gently, lost her vigor, and fell back quietly and slowly under the clay. Teig did to her as he had done to the man—he threw the clay back on her, and left the flags down overhead.

He began digging again near the door, but before he had thrown up more than a couple of shovelfuls, he noticed a man's hand laid bare by the spade. "By my soul, I'll go no further, then," said he to himself; "what use is it for me?" And he threw the clay in again on it, and settled the flags as they had been before.

He left the church then, and his heart was heavy enough, but he shut the door and locked it, and left the key where he found it. He sat down on a tombstone that was near the door, and began thinking. He was in great doubt what he should do. He laid his face between his two hands, and cried for grief and fatigue, since he was dead certain at this time that he never would come home alive. He made another attempt to loosen the hands of the corpse that were squeezed round his neck, but they were as tight as if they were clamped; and the more he tried to loosen them, the tighter they squeezed him. He was going to sit down once more, when the cold, horrid lips of the dead man said to him, "Carrick-fhad-vic-Orus," and he remembered the command of the good people to bring the corpse with him to that place if he should be unable to bury it where he had been.

He rose up, and looked about him. "I don't know the way," he said.

As soon as he had uttered the word, the corpse stretched out suddenly its left hand that had been tightened round his neck, and kept it pointing out, showing him the road he ought to follow. Teig went in the direction that the fingers were stretched, and passed out of the churchyard. He found himself on an old rutty, stony road, and he stood still again, not knowing where to turn. The corpse stretched out its bony hand a second time, and pointed out to him another road—not the road by which he had come when approaching the old church. Teig followed that road, and whenever he came to a path or road meeting it, the corpse always stretched out its hand and pointed with its fingers, showing him the way he was to take.

Many was the crossroad he turned down, and many was the crooked *boreen* he walked, until he saw from him an old burying-ground at last, beside the road, but there was neither church nor chapel nor any other building in it. The corpse squeezed him tightly, and he stood. "Bury me, bury me in the burying-ground," said the voice.

Teig drew over towards the old burying-place, and he was not more than about twenty yards from it, when, raising his eyes, he saw hundreds and hundreds of ghosts—men, women, and children—sitting on the top of the wall round about, or standing on the inside of it, or running backwards and forwards, and pointing at him, while he could see their mouths opening and shutting as if they were speaking, though he heard no word, nor any sound amongst them at all.

He was afraid to go forward, so he stood where he was, and the moment he stood, all the ghosts became quiet, and ceased moving. Then Teig understood that it was trying to keep him from going in, that they were. He walked a couple of yards forwards, and immediately the whole crowd rushed together towards the spot to which he was moving, and they stood so thickly together that it seemed to him that he never could break through them, even though he had a mind to try. But he had no mind to try it. He went back broken and dispirited, and when he had gone a couple of hundred yards from the burying-ground, he stood again, for he did not know what way he was to go. He heard the voice of the corpse in his ear, saying "Teampoll-Ronan," and the skinny hand was stretched out again, pointing him out the road.

As tired as he was, he had to walk, and the road was neither short nor even. The night was darker than ever, and it was difficult to make his way. Many was the toss he got, and many a bruise they left on his body. At last he saw Teampoll-Ronan from him in the distance, standing in the middle of the burying-ground. He moved over towards it, and thought he was all right and safe, when he saw no ghosts nor anything else on the wall, and he thought he would never be hindered now from leaving his load off him at last. He moved over to the gate, but as he was passing in, he tripped on the threshold. Before he could recover himself, something that he could not see seized him by the neck, by the hands, and by the feet, and bruised him, and shook him, and choked him, until he was nearly dead; and at last he was lifted up, and carried more than a hundred yards from that place, and then thrown down in an old dyke, with the corpse still clinging to him.

He rose up, bruised and sore, but feared to go near the place again, for he had seen nothing the time he was thrown down and carried away.

"You corpse, up on my back?" said he, "shall I go over again to the churchyard?"—but the corpse never answered him. "That's a sign you don't wish me to try it again," said Teig.

He was now in great doubt as to what he ought to do, when the corpse spoke in his ear, and said, "Imlogue-Fada."

"Oh, murder!" said Teig, "must I bring you there? If you keep me long walking like this, I tell you I'll fall under you."

He went on, however, in the direction the corpse pointed out to him. He could not have told, himself, how long he had been going, when the dead man behind suddenly squeezed him, and said, "There!"

Teig looked from him, and he saw a little low wall, that was so broken down in places that it was no wall at all. It was in a great wide field, in from the road; and only for three or four great stones at the corners, that were more like rocks than stones, there was nothing to show that there was either graveyard or burying-ground there.

"Is this Imlogue-Fada? Shall I bury you here?" said Teig.

"Yes," said the voice.

"But I see no grave or gravestone, only this pile of stones," said Teig.

The corpse did not answer, but stretched out its long fleshless hand to show Teig the direction in which he was to go. Teig went on accordingly, but he was greatly terrified, for he remembered what had happened to him at the last place. He went on, "with his heart in his mouth," as he said himself afterwards; but when he came to within fifteen or twenty yards of the little low square wall, there broke out a flash of lightning, bright yellow and red, with blue streaks in it, and went round about the wall in one course, and it swept by as fast as the swallow in the clouds, and the longer Teig remained looking at it the faster it went, till at last it became like a bright ring of flame round the old graveyard, which no one could pass without being burnt by it. Teig never saw, from the time he was born, and never saw afterwards, so wonderful or so splendid a sight as that was. Round went the flame, white and yellow and blue sparks leaping out from it as it went, and although at first it had been no more than a thin, narrow line, it increased slowly until it was at last a great broad band, and it was continually getting broader and higher, and throwing out more brilliant sparks, till there was never a color on the ridge of the earth that was not to be seen in that fire; and lightning never shone and flame never flamed that was so shining and so bright as that.

Teig was amazed; he was half dead with fatigue, and he had no courage left to approach the wall. There fell a mist over his eyes, and there came a *soorawn* in his head, and he was obliged to sit down upon a great stone to recover himself. He could see nothing but the light, and he could hear nothing but the whirr of it as it shot round the paddock faster than a flash of lightning.

As he sat there on the stone, the voice whispered once more in his ear, "Kill-Breedya"; and the dead man squeezed him so tightly that he cried out. He rose again, sick, tired, and trembling, and went forward as he was directed. The wind was cold, and the road was bad, and the load upon his back was heavy, and the night was dark, and he himself was nearly worn out, and if he had had very much farther to go he must have fallen dead under his burden.

At last the corpse stretched out its hand, and said to him, "Bury me there."

"This is the last burying-place," said Teig in his own mind; "and the little gray man said I'd be allowed to bury him in some of them, so it must be this; it can't be but they'll let him in here."

The first faint streak of the ring of day was appearing in the east, and the clouds were beginning to catch fire, but it was darker than ever, for the moon was set, and there were no stars.

"Make haste, make haste!" said the corpse; and Teig hurried forward as well as he could to the graveyard, which was a little place on a bare hill, with only a few graves in it. He walked boldly in through the open gate, and nothing touched him, nor did he either hear or see anything. He came to the middle of the ground, and then stood up and looked round him for a spade or shovel to make a grave. As he was turning round and searching, he suddenly perceived what startled him greatly—a newly-dug grave right before him. He moved over to it, and looked down, and there at the bottom he saw a black coffin. He clambered down into the hole and lifted the lid, and found that (as he thought it would be) the coffin was empty. He had hardly mounted up out of the hole, and was standing on the brink, when the corpse, which had clung to him for more than eight hours, suddenly relaxed its hold of his neck, and loosened its shins from round his hips, and sank down with a plop into the open coffin.

Teig fell down on his two knees at the brink of the grave, and gave thanks to God. He made no delay then, but pressed down the coffin lid in its place, and threw in the clay over it with his two hands, and when the grave was filled up, he stamped and leaped on it with his feet, until it was firm and hard, and then he left the place.

The sun was fast rising as he finished his work, and the first thing he did was to return to the road, and look out for a house to rest himself in. He found an inn at last; and lay down upon a bed there, and slept till night. Then he rose up and ate a little, and fell asleep again till morning. When he awoke in the morning he hired a horse and rode home. He was more than twenty-six miles from home where he was, and he had come all that way with the dead body on his back in one night.

All the people at his own home thought that he must have left the country, and they rejoiced greatly when they saw him come back. Everyone began asking him where he had been, but he would not tell anyone except his father.

He was a changed man from that day. He never drank too much; he never lost his money over cards; and especially he would not take the world and be out late by himself of a dark night.

He was not a fortnight at home until he married Mary, the girl he had been in love with, and it's at their wedding the sport was, and it's he was the happy man from that day forward, and it's all I wish that we may be as happy as he was.

GLOSSARY—*Rann,* a stanza; *kailee (céilidhe),* a visit in the evenings; *wirra (a mhuire),* "Oh, Mary!" an exclamation like the French *dame; rib,* a single hair (in Irish, *ribe); a lock (glac),* a bundle or wisp, or a little share of anything; *kippeen (cipín),* a rod or twig; *boreen (bóithrín),* a lane; *bodach,* a clown; *soorawn (suarán),* vertigo. *Avic (a Mhic)* = my son, or rather, Oh, son. *Mic* is the vocative of *Mac.*

The Haunted Cellar
Thomas Crofton Croker

THERE ARE FEW people who have not heard of the Mac-
Carthys—one of the real old Irish families, with the true
Milesian blood running in their veins as thick as buttermilk.
Many were the clans of this family in the south; as the Mac
Carthymore—and the Mac Carthy-reagh—and the Mac Carthy
of Muskerry; and all of them were noted for their hospitality to
strangers, gentle and simple.

But not one of that name, or of any other, exceeded Justin
Mac Carthy, of Ballinacarthy, at putting plenty to eat and drink
upon his table; and there was a right hearty welcome for
everyone who should share it with him. Many a wine cellar
would be ashamed of the name if that at Ballinacarthy was the
proper pattern for one. Large as that cellar was, it was crowded
with bins of wine, and long rows of pipes, and hogsheads, and
casks, that it would take more time to count than any sober man
could spare in such a place, with plenty to drink about him, and
a hearty welcome to do so.

There are many, no doubt, who will think that the butler
would have little to complain of in such a house; and the whole
country round would have agreed with them, if a man could be
found to remain as Mr. MacCarthy's butler for any length of
time worth speaking of; yet not one who had been in his service
gave him a bad word.

"We have no fault," they would say, "to find with the master,
and if he could but get anyone to fetch his wine from the cellar,
we might everyone of us have grown gray in the house and have
lived quiet and contented enough in his service until the end of
our days."

"'Tis a queer thing that, surely," thought young Jack Leary, a lad who had been brought up from a mere child in the stables of Ballinacarthy to assist in taking care of the horses, and had occasionally lent a hand in the butler's pantry:—"'Tis a mighty queer thing, surely, that one man after another cannot content himself with the best place in the house of a good master, but that everyone of them must quit, all through the means, as they say, of the wine cellar. If the master, long life to him! would but make me his butler, I warrant never the word more would be heard of grumbling at his bidding to go to the wine cellar."

Young Leary, accordingly, watched for what he conceived to be a favorable opportunity of presenting himself to the notice of his master.

A few mornings after, Mr. Mac Carthy went into his stableyard rather earlier than usual, and called loudly for the groom to saddle his horse, as he intended going out with the hounds. But there was no groom to answer, and young Jack Leary led Rainbow out of the stable.

"Where is William?" inquired Mr. Mac Carthy.

"Sir?" said Jack; and Mr. Mac Carthy repeated the question.

"Is it William, please your honor?" returned Jack; "why, then, to tell the truth, he had just *one* drop too much last night."

"Where did he get it?" said Mr. Mac Carthy; "for since Thomas went away the key of the wine cellar has been in my pocket, and I have been obliged to fetch what was drunk myself."

"Sorrow a know I know," said Leary, "unless the cook might have give him the *least taste* in life of whiskey. But," continued he, performing a low bow by seizing with his right hand a lock of hair, and pulling down his head by it, while his left leg, which had been put forward, was scraped back against the ground, "may I make so bold as just to ask your honor one question?"

"Speak out, Jack," said Mr. Mac Carthy.

"Why, then, does your honor want a butler?"

"Can you recommend me one," returned his master, with the smile of good-humor upon his countenance, "and one who will not be afraid of going to my wine cellar?"

"Is the wine cellar all the matter?" said young Leary; "devil a doubt I have of myself then for that."

"So you mean to offer me your services in the capacity of butler?" said Mr. Mac Carthy, with some surprise.

"Exactly so," answered Leary, now for the first time looking up from the ground.

"Well, I believe you to be a good lad, and have no objection to give you a trial."

"Long may your honor reign over us, and the Lord spare you to us!" ejaculated Leary, with another national bow, as his master rode off; and he continued for some time to gaze after him with a vacant stare, which slowly and gradually assumed a look of importance.

"Jack Leary," said he, at length, "Jack—is it Jack?" in a tone of wonder; "faith, 'tis not Jack now, but Mr. John, the butler;" and with an air of becoming consequence he strided out of the stable-yard towards the kitchen.

It is of little purport to my story, although it may afford an instructive lesson to the reader, to depict the sudden transition of nobody into somebody. Jack's former stable companion, a poor superannuated hound named Bran, who had been accustomed to receive many an affectionate pat on the head, was spurned from him with a kick and an "Out of the way, sirrah." Indeed, poor Jack's memory seemed sadly affected by this sudden change of situation. What established the point beyond all doubt was his almost forgetting the pretty face of Peggy, the kitchen wench, whose heart he had assailed but the preceding week by the offer of purchasing a gold ring for the fourth finger of her right hand, and a lusty imprint of good-will upon her lips.

When Mr. Mac Carthy returned from hunting, he sent for Jack Leary—so he still continued to call his new butler. "Jack," said he, "I believe you are a trustworthy lad, and here are the keys of my cellar. I have asked the gentlemen with whom I hunted today to dine with me, and I hope they may be satisfied at the way in which you will wait on them at table; but, above all, let there be no want of wine after dinner."

Mr. John having a tolerably quick eye for such things, and being naturally a handy lad, spread his cloth accordingly, laid his plates and knives and forks in the same manner he had seen his predecessors in office perform these mysteries, and really, for the first time, got through attendance on dinner very well.

It must not be forgotten, however, that it was at the house of an Irish country squire, who was entertaining a company of booted and spurred fox-hunters, not very particular about what are considered matters of infinite importance under other circumstances and in other societies.

For instance, few of Mr. Mac Carthy's guests (though all excellent and worthy men in their way) cared much whether the punch produced after soup was made of Jamaica or Antigua rum; some even would not have been inclined to question the correctness of good old Irish whiskey; and, with the exception of their liberal host himself, every one in company preferred the port which Mr. Mac Carthy put on his table to the less ardent flavor of claret—a choice rather at variance with modern sentiment.

It was waxing near midnight, when Mr. Mac Carthy rung the bell three times. This was a signal for more wine; and Jack proceeded to the cellar to procure a fresh supply, but it must be confessed not without some little hesitation.

The luxury of ice was then unknown in the south of Ireland; but the superiority of cool wine had been acknowledged by all men of sound judgment and true taste.

The grandfather of Mr. Mac Carthy, who had built the mansion of Ballinacarthy upon the site of an old castle which had belonged to his ancestors, was fully aware of this important fact; and in the construction of his magnificent wine cellar had availed himself of a deep vault, excavated out of the solid rock in former times as a place of retreat and security. The descent to this vault was by a flight of steep stone stairs, and here and there in the wall were narrow passages—I ought rather to call them crevices; and also certain projections, which cast deep shadows, and looked very frightful when anyone went down the cellar stairs with a single light: indeed, two lights did not much improve the matter, for though the breadth of the shadows became less, the narrow crevices remained as dark and darker than ever.

Summoning up all his resolution, down went the new butler, bearing in his right hand a lantern and the key of the cellar, and in his left a basket, which he considered sufficiently capacious to contain an adequate stock for the remainder of the evening: he arrived at the door without any interruption whatever; but when he put the key, which was of an ancient and clumsy kind—for it was before the days of Bramah's patent—and turned it in the lock, he thought he heard a strange kind of laughing within the cellar, to which some empty bottle that stood upon the floor outside vibrated so violently that they struck against each other: in this he could not be mistaken, although he may have been deceived in the laugh, for the bottles were just at his feet, and he saw them in motion.

Leary paused for a moment, and looked about him with becoming caution. He then boldly seized the handle of the key,

and turned it with all his strength in the lock, as if he doubted his own power of doing so; and the door flew open with a most tremendous crash, that if the house had not been built upon the solid rock would have shook it from the foundation.

To recount what the poor fellow saw would be impossible, for he seems not to have known very clearly himself: but what he told the cook next morning was, that he heard a roaring and bellowing like a mad bull, and that all the pipes and hogsheads and casks in the cellar went rocking backwards and forwards with so much force that he thought everyone would have been staved in, and that he should have been drowned or smothered in wine.

When Leary recovered, he made his way back as well as he could to the dining room, where he found his master and the company very impatient for his return.

"What kept you?" said Mr. Mac Carthy in an angry voice; "and where is the wine? I rung for it half an hour since."

"The wine is in the cellar, I hope, sir," said Jack, trembling violently; "I hope 'tis not all lost."

"What do you mean, fool?" exclaimed Mr. Mac Carthy in a still more angry tone: "why did you not fetch some with you?"

Jack looked wildly about him, and only uttered a deep groan.

"Gentlemen," said Mr. Mac Carthy to his guests, "this is too much. When I next see you to dinner, I hope it will be in another house, for it is impossible I can remain longer in this, where a man has no command over his own wine cellar, and cannot get a butler to do his duty. I have long thought of moving from Ballinacarthy; and I am now determined, with the blessing of God, to leave it tomorrow. But wine shall you have were I to go myself to the cellar for it." So saying, he rose from table, took the key and lantern from his half-stupified servant, who regarded him with a look of vacancy, and descended the narrow stairs, already described, which led to his cellar.

When he arrived at the door, which he found open, he thought he heard a noise, as if of rats or mice scrambling over the casks, and on advancing perceived a little figure, about six inches in height, seated astride upon the pipe of the oldest port in the place, and bearing a spigot upon his shoulder. Raising the lantern, Mr. Mac Carthy contemplated the little fellow with wonder: he wore a red night-cap on his head; before him was a short leather apron, which now, from his attitude, fell rather on one side; and he had stockings of a light blue color, so long as nearly to cover the entire of his leg; with shoes, having huge silver buckles in them, and with high heels (perhaps out of vanity to make him appear taller). His face was like a withered winter apple; and his nose, which was of a bright crimson color, about the tip wore a delicate purple bloom, like that of a plum; yet his eyes twinkled

> "like those mites
> Of candied dew in money nights—"

and his mouth twitched up at one side with an arch grin.

"Ha, scoundrel!" exclaimed Mr. Mac Carthy, "have I found you at last? disturber of my cellar—what are you doing there?"

"Sure, and master," returned the little fellow, looking up at him with one eye, and with the other throwing a sly glance towards the spigot on his shoulder, "a'n't we going to move tomorrow? and sure you would not leave your own little Cluricaune Naggeneen behind you?"

"Oh!" thought Mr. MacCarthy, "if you are to follow me, master Naggeneen, I don't see much use in quitting Ballinacarthy." So filling with wine the basket which young Leary in his fright had left behind him, and locking the cellar door, he rejoined his guests.

For some years after Mr. Mac Carthy had always to fetch the

wine for his table himself, as the little Cluricaune Naggeneen seemed to feel a personal respect towards him. Notwithstanding the labor of these journeys, the worthy lord of Ballinacarthy lived in his paternal mansion to a good round age, and was famous to the last for the excellence of his wine, and conviviality of his company; but at the time of his death, the same conviviality had nearly emptied his wine cellar; and as it was never so well filled again, nor so often visited, the revels of master Naggeneen became less celebrated, and are now only spoken of among the legendary lore of the country. It is even said that the poor little fellow took the declension of the cellar so to heart, that he became negligent and careless of himself, and that he has been sometimes seen going about with hardly a *skreed* to cover him.

Far Darrig in Donegal
Letitia Maclintock

PAT DIVER, the tinker, was a man well accustomed to a wandering life, and to strange shelters; he had shared the beggar's blanket in smoky cabins; he had crouched beside the still in many a nook and corner where poteen was made on the wild Innishowen mountains; he had even slept on the bare heather, or on the ditch, with no roof over him but the vault of heaven; yet were all his nights of adventure tame and common-place when compared with one especial night.

During the day preceding that night, he had mended all the kettles and saucepans in Moville and Greencastle, and was on his way to Culdaff, when night overtook him on a lonely mountain road.

He knocked at one door after another asking for a night's lodging, while he jingled the halfpence in his pocket, but was everywhere refused.

Where was the boasted hospitality of Innishowen, which he had never before known to fail? It was of no use to be able to pay when the people seemed so churlish. Thus thinking, he made his way toward a light a little further on, and knocked at another cabin door.

An old man and woman were seated one at each side of the fire.

"Will you be pleased to give me a night's lodging, sir?" asked Pat respectfully.

"Can you tell a story?" returned the old man.

"No, then, sir, I canna say I'm good at story-telling" replied the puzzled tinker.

"Then you maun just gang further, for none but them that can

71

tell a story will get in here."

This reply was made in so decided a tone that Pat did not attempt to repeat his appeal, but turned away reluctantly to resume his weary journey.

"A story, indeed," muttered he. "Auld wives fables to please the weans!"

As he took up his bundle of tinkering implements, he observed a barn standing rather behind the dwelling house, and, aided by the rising moon, he made his way toward it.

It was a clean, roomy barn, with a piled-up heap of straw in one corner. Here was a shelter not to be despised; so Pat crept under the straw, and was soon asleep.

He could not have slept very long when he was awakened by the tramp of feet, and, peeping cautiously through a crevice in his straw covering, he saw four immensely tall men enter the barn, dragging a body, which they threw roughly upon the floor.

They next lighted a fire in the middle of the barn, and fastened the corpse by the feet with a great rope to a beam in the roof. One of them then began to turn it slowly before the fire. "Come on," said he, addressing a gigantic fellow, the tallest of the four—"I'm tired; you be to tak' your turn."

"Faix an' troth, I'll no turn him," replied the big man. "There's Pat Diver in under the straw, why wouldn't he tak' his turn?"

With hideous clamor the four men called the wretched Pat, who, seeing there was no escape, thought it was his wisest plan to come forth as he was bidden.

"Now, Pat," said they, "you'll turn the corpse, but if you let him burn you'll be tied up there and roasted in his place."

Pat's hair stood on end, and the cold perspiration poured from his forehead, but there was nothing for it but to perform his dreadful task.

Seeing him fairly embarked in it, the tall men went away.

Soon, however, the flames rose so high as to singe the rope, and the corpse fell with a great thud upon the fire, scattering the ashes and embers, and extracting a howl of anguish from the miserable cook, who rushed to the door, and ran for his life.

He ran on until he was ready to drop with fatigue, when, seeing a drain overgrown with tall, rank grass, he thought he would creep in there and lie hidden till morning.

But he was not many minutes in the drain before he heard the heavy tramping again, and the four men came up with their burthen, which they laid down on the edge of the drain.

"I'm tired," said one, to the giant; "it's your turn to carry him a piece now."

"Faix and troth, I'll no carry him," replied he, "but there's Pat Diver in the drain, why wouldn't he come out and tak' his turn?"

"Come out, Pat, come out," roared all the men, and Pat, almost dead with fright, crept out.

He staggered on under the weight of the corpse until he reached Kiltown Abbey, a ruin festooned with ivy, where the brown owl hooted all night long, and the forgotten dead slept around the walls under dense, matted tangles of brambles and ben-weed.

No one ever buried there now, but Pat's tall companions turned into the wild graveyard, and began digging a grave.

Pat, seeing them thus engaged, thought he might once more try to escape, and climbed up into a hawthorn tree in the fence, hoping to be hidden in the boughs.

"I'm tired," said the man who was digging the grave; "here, take the spade," addressing the big man, "it's your turn."

"Faix an' troth, it's no my turn," replied he, as before. "There's Pat Diver in the tree, why wouldn't he come down and tak' his turn?"

Pat came down to take the spade, but just then the cocks in the little farmyards and cabins round the abbey began to crow, and the men looked at one another.

"We must go," said they, "and well is it for you, Pat Diver, that the cocks crowed, for if they had not, you'd just ha' been bundled into that grave with the corpse."

Two months passed, and Pat had wandered far and wide over the county Donegal, when he chanced to arrive at Raphoe during a fair.

Among the crowd that filled the Diamond he came suddenly on the big man.

"How are you, Pat Diver?" said he, bending down to look into the tinker's face.

"You've the advantage of me, sir, for I havna' the pleasure of knowing you," faltered Pat.

"Do you not know me, Pat?" Whisper—"When you go back to Innishowen, you'll have a story to tell!"

The Lepracaun; or, Fairy Shoemaker

William Allingham

I

LITTLE Cowboy, what have you heard,
Up on the lonely rath's green mound?
Only the plaintive yellow bird
Sighing in sultry fields around,
Chary, chary, chary, chee-ee!—
Only the grasshopper and the bee?—
"Tip tap, rip-rap,
Tick-a-tack-too!
Scarlet leather, sewn together,
This will make a shoe.
Left, right, pull it tight;
Summer days are warm;
Underground in winter,
Laughing at the storm!"
Lay your ear close to the hill.
Do you not catch the tiny clamor,
Busy click of an elfin hammer,
Voice of the Lepracaun singing shrill
As he merrily plies his trade?
He's a span
And a quarter in height.
Get him in sight, hold him tight,
And you're a made
Man!

II

You watch your cattle the summer day,
Sup on potatoes, sleep in the hay;
How would you like to roll in your carriage,
Look for a duchess's daughter in marriage?
Seize the Shoemaker—then you may!
"Big boots a-hunting,
Sandles in the hall,
White for a wedding-feast,
Pink for a ball.
This way, that way,
So we make a shoe;
Getting rich every stitch,
Tick-tack-too!"
Nine-and-ninety treasure-crocks
This keen miser-fairy hath
Hid in mountains, woods and rocks,
Ruin and round-tow'r, cave and rath,
And where the cormorants build;
From times of old
Guarded by him;
Each of them fill'd
Full to the brim
With gold!

III

I caught him at work one day, myself,
In the castle-ditch, where foxglove grows,—
A wrinkled, wizen'd, and bearded Elf,
Spectacles stuck on his pointed nose,
Silver buckles to his hose,
Leather apron—shoe in his lap—

"Rip-rap, tip-tap,
Tick-tack-too!
(A grasshopper on my cap!
Away the moth flew!)
Buskins for a fairy prince,
Brogues for his son,—
Pay me well, pay me well,
When the job is done!"
The rogue was mine, beyond a doubt.
I stared at him; he stared at me;
"Servant, Sir!" "Humph!" says he,
And pull'd a snuff-box out.
He took a long pinch, look'd better pleased,
The queer little Lepracaun;
Offer'd the box with a whimsical grace,—
Pouf! he flung the dust in my face,
And, while I sneezed,
Was gone!

From The Crock of Gold
James Stephens

WHEN THE LEPRECAUN came through the pine wood on the
following day he met the two children at a little distance from
the house. He raised his open right hand above his head (this is
both the fairy and the Gaelic form of salutation), and would
have passed on but that a thought brought him to a halt. Sitting
down before the two children he stared at them for a long time,
and they stared back at him. At last he said to the boy:

"What is your name, a vic vig O?"

"Seumas Beg, sir," the boy replied.

"It's a little name," said the Leprecaun.

"It's what my mother calls me, sir," returned the boy.

"What does your father call you," was the next question.

"Seumas Eoghan Maelduin O'Carbhail Mac an Droid."

"It's a big name," said the Leprecaun, and he turned to the
little girl. "What is your name, a cailin vig O?"

"Brigid Beg, sir."

"And what does your father call you?"

"He never calls me at all, sir."

"Well, Seumaseen and Breedeen, you are good little children,
and I like you very much. Health be with you until I come to see
you again."

And then the Leprecaun went back the way he had come. As
he went he made little jumps and cracked his fingers, and
sometimes he rubbed one leg against the other.

"That's a nice Leprecaun," said Seumas.

"I like him too," said Brigid.

"Listen," said Seumas, "let me be the Leprecaun, and you be
the two children, and I will ask you our names."

So they did that.

The next day the Leprecaun came again. He sat down beside the children and, as before, he was silent for a little time.

"Are you not going to ask us our names, sir?" said Seumas.

His sister smoothed out her dress shyly.

"My name, sir, is Brigid Beg," said she.

"Did you ever play Jackstones?" said the Leprecaun.

"No, sir," replied Seumas.

"I'll teach you how to play Jackstones," said the Leprecaun, and he picked up some pine cones and taught the children that game.

"Did you ever play Ball in the Decker?"

"No, sir," said Seumas.

"Did you ever play 'I can make a nail with my ree-ro-raddy-O, I can make a nail with my ree-ro-ray?'"

"No, sir," replied Seumas.

"It's a nice game," said the Leprecaun, "and so is Cap-on-the-back, and Twenty-four yards on the billy-goat's tail, and Towns, and Relievo, and Leap-frog. I'll teach you all these games," said the Leprecaun, "and I'll teach you how to play Knifey, and Hole-and-taw, and Horneys and Robbers."

"Leap-frog is the best one to start with, so I'll teach it to you at once. Let you bend down like this, Breedeen, and you bend down like that a good distance away, Seumas. Now I jump over Breedeen's back, and then I run and jump over Seumaseen's back like this, and then I run ahead again and I bend down. Now, Breedeen, you jump over your brother, and then you jump over me, and run a good bit on and bend down again. Now, Seumas, it is your turn; you jump over me and then over your sister, and then you run on and bend down again and I jump.

"This is a fine game, sir," said Seumas.

"It is, a vic vig,—keep in your head," said the Leprecaun.

"That's a good jump, you couldn't beat that jump, Seumas."

"I can jump better than Brigid already," replied Seumas, "and I'll jump as well as you do when I get more practice— keep in your head, sir."

Almost without noticing it they had passed through the edge of the wood, and were playing into a rough field which was cumbered with big, gray rocks. It was the very last field in sight, and behind it the rough, heather-packed mountain sloped distantly away to the skyline. There was a raggedy blackberry hedge all round the field, and there were long, tough, haggard-looking plants growing in clumps here and there. Near a corner of this field there was a broad, low tree, and as they played they came near and nearer to it. The Leprecaun gave a back very close to the tree. Seumas ran and jumped and slid down a hole at the side of the tree. Then Brigid ran and jumped and slid down the same hole

"Dear me!" said Brigid, and she flashed out of sight.

The Leprecaun cracked his fingers and rubbed one leg against the other, and then he also dived into the hole and disappeared from view.

When the time at which the children usually went home had passed, the Thin Woman of Inis Magrath became a little anxious. She had never known them to be late for dinner before. There was one of the children whom she hated; it was her own child, but as she had forgotten which of them was hers, and as she loved one of them, she was compelled to love both for fear of making a mistake, and chastising the child for whom her heart secretly yearned. Therefore, she was equally concerned about both of them.

Dinner time passed and supper time arrived, but the children did not. Again and again the Thin Woman went out through the dark pine trees and called until she was so hoarse that she could not even hear herself when she roared. The evening wore on to the night, and while she waited for the Philosopher to come in she reviewed the situation. Her husband had not come in, the children had not come in, the Leprecaun had not returned as arranged. . . . A light flashed upon her. The Leprecaun had kidnapped her children! She announced a vengeance against the Leprecauns, which would stagger humanity. While in the extreme center of her ecstasy the Philosopher came through the trees and entered the house.

The Thin Woman flew to him—

"Husband," said she, "the Leprecauns of Gort na Cloca Mora have kidnapped our children."

The Philosopher gazed at her for a moment.

"Kidnapping," said he, "has been for many centuries a favorite occupation of fairies, gypsies, and the brigands of the East. The usual procedure is to attach a person and hold it to ransom. If the ransom is not paid an ear or a finger may be cut from the captive and despatched to those interested, with the statement that an arm or a leg will follow in a week unless suitable arrangements are entered into."

"Do you understand," said the Thin Woman passionately, "that it is your own children who have been kidnapped?"

"I do not," said the Philosopher. "This course, however, is rarely followed by the fairy people: they do not ordinarily steal for ransom, but for love of thieving, or from some other obscure and possibly functional causes, and the victim is retained in their forts or duns until by the effluxion of time they forget their origin and become peaceable citizens of the fairy state. Kidnapping is not by any means confined to either humanity or the fairy people."

"Monster," said the Thin Woman in a deep voice, "will you listen to me?"

"I will not," said the Philosopher. "Many of the insectivora also practice this custom. Ants, for example, are a respectable race living in well-ordered communities. They have attained to a most complex and artificial civilization, and will frequently adventure far afield on colonizing or other expeditions from whence they return with a rich booty of aphides and other stock, who thenceforward become the servants and domestic creatures of the republic. As they neither kill nor eat their captives, this practice will be termed kidnapping. The same may be said of bees, a hardy and industrious race living in hexagonal cells which are very difficult to make. Sometimes, on lacking a queen of their own, they have been observed to abduct one from a less powerful neighbor, and use her for their own purposes without shame, mercy, or remorse."

"Will you not understand?" screamed the Thin Woman.

"I will not," said the Philosopher. "Semitropical apes have been rumored to kidnap children, and are reported to use them very tenderly indeed, sharing their coconuts, yams, plantains, and other equatorial provender with the largest generosity, and conveying their delicate captives from tree to tree (often at great distances from each other and from the ground) with the most guarded solicitude and benevolence."

"1 am going to bed," said the Thin Woman; "your stirabout is on the hob."

"Are there lumps in it, my dear?" said the Philosopher.

"I hope there are," replied the Thin Woman, and she leaped into bed. That night the Philosopher was afflicted with the most extraordinary attack of rheumatism he had ever known, nor did he get any ease until the gray morning wearied his lady into a reluctant slumber.

·   ·   ·   ·   ·

The Thin Woman of Inis Magrath slept very late that morning, but when she did awaken her impatience was so urgent that she could scarcely delay to eat her breakfast. Immediately after she had eaten she put on her bonnet and shawl and went through the pine wood in the direction of Gort na Cloca Mora. In a short time she reached the rocky field, and, walking over to the tree in the southeast corner, she picked up a small stone and hammered loudly against the trunk of the tree. She hammered in a peculiar fashion, giving two knocks and then three knocks, and then one knock. A voice came up from the hole.

"Who is that, please?" said the voice.

"Ban na Droid of Inis Magrath, and well you know it," was her reply.

"I am coming up, Noble Woman," said the voice, and in another moment the Leprecaun leaped out of the hole.

"Where are Seumas and Brigid Beg?" said the Thin Woman sternly.

"How would I know where they are," replied the Leprecaun. "Wouldn't they be at home now?"

"If they were at home I wouldn't have come here looking for them," was her reply. "It is my belief that you have them."

"Search me," said the Leprecaun, opening his waistcoat.

"They are down there in your little house," said the Thin Woman angrily, "and the sooner you let them up the better it will be for yourself and your five brothers."

"Noble Woman," said the Leprecaun, "you can go down yourself into our little house and look. I can't say fairer than that."

"I wouldn't fit down there," said she. " I'm too big."

"You know the way for making yourself little," replied the Leprecaun.

"But I mightn't be able to make myself big again," said the Thin Woman, "and then you and your dirty brothers would have it all your own way. If you don't let the children up," she continued, "I'll raise the Shee of Croghan Conghaile against you. You know what happened to the Cluricauns of Oilean na Glas when they stole the Queen's baby—It will be a worse thing than that for you. If the children are not back in my house before moonrise this night, I'll go round to my people. Just tell that to your five ugly brothers. Health with you," she added, and strode away.

"Health with yourself, Noble Woman," said the Leprecaun, and he stood on one leg until she was out of sight and then he slid down into the hole again.

·　　·　　·　　·　　·

When the children leaped into the hole at the foot of the tree they found themselves sliding down a dark, narrow slant which dropped them softly enough into a little room. This room was hollowed out immediately under the tree, and great care had been taken not to disturb any of the roots which ran here and there through the chamber in the strangest criss-cross, twisted fashion. To get across such a place one had to walk round, and jump over, and duck under perpetually. Some of the roots had formed themselves very conveniently into low seats and narrow, uneven tables, and at the bottom all the roots ran into the floor and away again in the direction required by their business. After the clear air outside this place was very dark to the children's eyes, so that they could not see anything for a few minutes, but after a little time their eyes became accustomed to the semiobscurity and they were able to see quite well. The first things they became aware of were six small men who were seated on low roots. They were all dressed in tight green clothes and little leathern aprons, and they wore tall green hats which wobbled when they moved. They were all busily engaged making shoes. One was drawing out wax ends on his knee, another was softening pieces of leather in a bucket of water, another was polishing the instep of a shoe with a piece of curved bone, another was paring down a heel with a short broad-bladed knife, and another was hammering wooden pegs into a sole. He had all the pegs in his mouth, which gave him a wide-faced, jolly expression, and according as a peg was wanted he blew it into his hand and hit it twice with his hammer, and then he blew another peg, and he always blew the peg with the right end uppermost, and never had to hit it more than twice. He was a person well worth watching.

The children had slid down so unexpectedly that they almost forgot their good manners, but as soon as Seumas Beg discovered that he was really in a room he removed his cap and stood up.

"God be with all here," said he.

The Leprecaun who had brought them lifted Brigid from the floor to which amazement still constrained her.

"Sit down on that little root, child of my heart," said he, "and you can knit stockings for us."

"Yes, sir," said Brigid meekly.

The Leprecaun took four knitting needles and a ball of green wool from the top of a high, horizontal root. He had to climb over one, go round three, and climb up two roots to get at it, and he did this so easily that it did not seem a bit of trouble. He gave the needles and wool to Brigid Beg.

"Do you know how to turn the heel Brigid Beg?" said he.

"No, sir," said Brigid.

"Well, I'll show you how when you come to it."

The other six Leprecauns had ceased work and were looking at the children. Seumas turned to them.

"God bless the work," said he politely.

One of the Leprecauns, who had a gray, puckered face and a thin fringe of gray whisker very far under his chin, then spoke.

"Come over here, Seumas Beg," said he, "and I'll measure you for a pair of shoes. Put your foot up on that root."

The boy did so, and the Leprecaun took the measure of his foot with a wooden rule.

"Now, Brigid Beg, show me your foot," and he measured her also. "They'll be ready for you in the morning."

"Do you never do anything else but make shoes, sir?" said Seumas.

"We do not," replied the Leprecaun, "except when we want new clothes, and then we have to make them, but we grudge every minute spent making anything else except shoes, because that is the proper work for a Leprecaun. In the nighttime we go about the country into people's houses and we clip little pieces off their money, and so, bit by bit, we get a crock of gold together, because, do you see, a Leprecaun has to have a crock of gold so that if he's captured by menfolk he may be able to ransom himself. But that seldom happens, because it's a great disgrace altogether to be captured by a man, and we've practiced so long dodging among the roots here that we can easily get away from them. Of course, now and again we are caught; but men are fools, and we always escape without having to pay the ransom at all. We wear green clothes because it's the color of the grass and the leaves, and when we sit down under a bush or lie in the grass they just walk by without noticing us."

"Will you let me see your crock of gold?" said Seumas.

The Leprecaun looked at him fixedly for a moment.

"Do you like griddle bread and milk?" said he.

"I like it well," Seumas answered.

"Then you had better have some," and the Leprecaun took a piece of griddle bread from the shelf and filled two saucers with milk.

While the children were eating the Leprecauns asked them many questions—

"What time do you get up in the morning?"

"Seven o'clock," replied Seumas.

"And what do you have for breakfast?"

"Stirabout and milk," he replied.

"It's good food," said the Leprecaun. "What do you have for dinner?"

"Potatoes and milk," said Seumas.

"It's not bad at all," said the Leprecaun. "And what do you have for supper?"

Brigid answered this time because her brother's mouth was full.

"Bread and milk, sir," said she.

"There's nothing better," said the Leprecaun.

"And then we go to bed," continued Brigid.

"Why wouldn't you?" said the Leprecaun.

It was at this point the Thin Woman of Inis Magrath knocked on the tree trunk and demanded that the children should be returned to her.

When she had gone away the Leprecauns held a consultation, whereat it was decided that they could not afford to anger the Thin Woman and the Shee of Croghan Conghaile so they shook hands with the children and bade them good-bye. The Leprecaun who had enticed them away from home brought them back again, and on parting he begged the children to visit Gort na Cloca Mora whenever they felt inclined.

"There's always a bit of griddle bread or potato cake, and a noggin of milk for a friend," said he.

"You are very kind, sir," replied Seumas, and his sister said the same words.

As the Leprecaun walked away they stood watchlng him.

"Do you remember," said Seumas, "the way he hopped and waggled his leg the last time he was here?"

"I do so," replied Brigid.

"Well he isn't hopping or doing anything at all this time," said Seumas.

"He's not in good humor tonight," said Brigid, "but I like him."

"So do I," said Seumas.

When they went into the house the Thin Woman of Inis Magrath was very glad to see them, and she baked a cake with currants in it, and also gave them both stirabout and potatoes; but the Philosopher did not notice that they had been away at all. He said at last that "talking was bad wit, that women were always making a fuss, that children should be fed, but not fattened, and that beds were meant to be slept in." The Thin Woman replied "that he was a grisly old man without bowels, that she did not know what she had married him for, that he was three times her age, and that no one would believe what she had to put up with."

The Gollan
A. E. Coppard

THERE WAS ONCE a peasant named Goose who had worked his back crooked with never a Thank-ye from Providence or Man, and he had a son, Gosling, whom the neighbors called The Gollan for short. The Gollan was an obedient child and strong, though not by nature very willing. He was so obedient that he would do without question whatever anybody told him to do. One day he was bringing his mother three eggs in a basket and he met a rude boy.

"Hoi," called the rude boy, "are those eggs the bouncing eggs?"

"Are they?" enquired The Gollan.

"Try one and see," the rude boy said.

The Gollan took one of the eggs from the basket and dropped it to the ground, and it broke.

"Haw!" complained the rude one, "you did not do it properly. How could an egg bounce if you dropped it so? You must throw it hard and it will fly back into your hand like a bird."

So The Gollan took another and dashed it to the ground and waited. But the egg only lay spilled at his feet.

"No, no, no! Stupid fellow!" the rude boy cried. "Look. Throw the other one up in the air high as you can and all three will bounce back into your basket."

So The Gollan threw the last egg up on high, but it only dropped beside the others and all lay in a slop of ruins.

"Oh dear! What will my mother say? Oh dear!" wept The Gollan.

The rude boy merely put his thumb to his nose and ran off upon his proper business, laughing.

The Gollan grew up a great powerful fellow, and whatever anyone told him to do, it might be simple, it might be hard, he did it without repining, which shows that he had a kind heart anyway, though he had little enough inclination to work; indeed he had no wish to at all.

One day his father said to him: "My son, you are full of strength and vigor, you are the prop of my old age and the apple of my two eyes. Take now these five and twenty pigs and go you to market and dispose of them. Beware of false dealing, and you may hear wonders."

"What wonders should I hear?"

"Mum," said his father, "is the word. Say nothing and scare nobody."

He gave him two noggins of ale and off went The Gollan. And it was a queer half and half day, however, but full of color. There were poppies in the green corn, charlock in the swedes, and weak sunlight in the opaline sky. He tried to drive the pigs but they had their minds set upon some other matters and would not go where they should because of distractions and interruptions. There was the green corn, there were the swedes, and there were heifers in the lane, lambs afield, and hens in every hedge, so before he had gone a mile the pigs were all astray.

"I don't care where those pigs go," then said The Gollan to himself. "I don't trouble about those pigs as long as I have my strength and vigor." So he lay down under a nut hazel-bush and was soon sleeping.

In the course of time—long or short makes no odds—he heard someone whistling shrilly, and waking up he looked about him to the right hand and to the left and soon saw a person caught hard and fast in a catchpole, a little plump man with a red beard and bright buckled shoes.

"Well met, friend!" the little man called out. "Pray release me from this trap and I will make your fortune." So The Gollan went and put out all his strength and vigor, with a heave and a hawk and a crash, until he had drawn the little plump man out of the trap and set him free.

"Thanks, friend," said the leprechaun—for he was that and no less, not like any man you ever read about. "You have done me a kind service. Ask any reward you will and I will give it."

"Sir," said the Gollan, "there is no matter about that. I am the prop of my father's age and the apple of his two eyes. I have strength and vigor with which I work for what I need."

"Unhappy is that man," the leprechaun answered, "who serves his need and not his choice. You have strength and vigor, but how do you use it?"

The Gollan drew himself up proudly: "I can crack rocks and hew trees."

"Well, then," replied the other, "crack on, and hew."

"Alas," The Gollan explained, "I have four fingers and a thumb on one hand, four fingers and a thumb on the other, all of them able—but not one of them willing." And he confided to the leprechaun that it was his doom and distress to be at the beck and call of everyone because of his strength and vigor, and he with no heart to refuse to do a deed required of him.

"That cannot be endured. I can easily remedy it," said the leprechaun. "I will make you invisible to mankind, except only when you are asleep. Nobody will be able to see you when you are awake and walking, therefore they will not be able to give you a task of any kind."

So he made The Gollan invisible there and then, and no one saw The Gollan any more, save his parents when he was sleeping, and his life became a bed or roses and a bower of bliss. Where is The Gollan?—people would say. But though they knew he was thereabout they could not set eyes on him and they could not find him. If The Gollan were only with us—they would say—he would do this tiresome labor, he would do it well. But as he was no longer visible to them they could not catch him and they could not ask him. The Gollan would be about in the sunlight day after day doing nothing at all, and got so blown up with pride that he thought:

"I am invisible, no one can task me in my strength and vigor. I am king of all the unseen world, and that is as good as twenty of these other kings. I live as I choose, and I take my need as I want it."

But though it was all very grand to be invisible The Gollan soon found out that there was small blessing in it. He could be seen by none save when he slept, but the truth is neither could he see anybody—man, woman, or child. No one could hear him, but then he himself could hear no one—man, woman, or child. It was the same way with smelling, touching and tasting. Animals and birds he could see, and he could talk to them, but they were so hard of understanding that he might as well have conversed with a monument or a door. Sure, he had kept his wits but he had lost his five senses, and that is cruel fortune.

After a while his heart grew weary for the sight of his friends and the talk and sounds of people, he was tired of seeing animals and birds only, so he went to a hawk he knew that had the most piercing gaze, and said:

"Friend, lend me your two eyes for a while and I will pawn you my own for their safe return."

"Will I? Will I?" mused the hawk.

"You will!" The Gollan sternly said.

So they exchanged, but The Gollan was greatly deceived by these hawk eyes. He went about wearing them far and near, and he saw thousands of mice and birds and moles, but those eyes never set their gaze on a single human creature, good, bad, or medium. What was worse, rascally things, they never seemed to want to! The farther he wandered the more sure it became that those eyes were merely looking out for moles and voles and such like. He saw nothing else except a jackass with fine upstanding ears straying in a bethistled waste whom he accosted:

"Friend, lend me your two ears for a while. I will pawn you my own for their safe return."

"Will you? Won't you?" mused the ass.

"I will," declared The Gollan, for he longed to hear human speech again, or a song to cheer him.

So they exchanged. But The Gollan was more deceived and bewildered than ever, for he never caught the sound of any pleasant human talk. What he heard was only an ass's bald portion, vile oaths, denunciations, and abuse. And although it all rushed into one ear and quickly fell out of the other, it was not good hearing at all; it was not satisfactory. When he heard a pig grunting not far off he hastened to the pig, saying:

"Friend, lend me your nose. I will pawn you mine for its safe return."

"Ask me no more," said the pig, surveying him with a rueful smile as he suffered The Gollan to make the exchange.

But something kept The Gollan from smelling anything save what a pig may smell. Instead of flowers, the odor of fruit, or the cook's oven, the swinish nostrils delighted only in the vapors of swill and offal and ordure. Surely—thought The Gollan—it is better to be invisible and senseless than to live thus. So he tried no further, but gave back the eyes, the ears, and the nose and received his pledges again.

Now at that time the king of the land was much put about by the reason of a little pond that lay in front of his palace. It was a meager patch of water and no ways good.

"If only this were a lake," sighed the king, "a great lake of blue water with neat waves and my ships upon it and my swans roving and my snipe calling and my fish going to and fro, my realm would be a great realm and the envy of the whole world."

And one day, as he was wandering and wondering what he could do about this, he came upon The Gollan lying on a green bank drowsing and dreaming. Of course when the king set eyes on him, he saw him and knew him.

"Hoi, Gollan!" the king roared at him. "Stretch out that water for me!" Just like that. The Gollan woke up and at once became invisible again, but he was so startled at being roared at that without thinking, just absent-mindedly, he stretched out the water of the king's pond and there and then it became a fine large lake with neat waves and ships and swans and such like, beautiful—though when he learned the right of it The Gollan was crabby and vexed, "I am the king of the unseen world, and that's as good as any twenty of these other kings." Still, he could not alter it back again. Whatever he did had to stay as it was once done: it could neither be changed nor improved.

However, by the reason of his fine new lake and ships the king's realm became the envy of all other nations, who began to strive after it and attack it. The king was not much of a one for martial dispositions and so the whole of his country was soon beleaguered and the people put to miserable extravagances.

Now although The Gollan could not directly see or hear anything of this, yet one way and another he came to know something of the misfortune, and then he was worn to a tatter with rage and fury by the reason he was such a great one for the patriotism. And he was powerless to help now his five senses were gone from him.

"O, what sort of a game is this," he thought, "now the world is in ruins and I have no more senses than a ghost or a stone! I had the heart of an ass when I took that red-haired villain out of his trap and had his reward. Reward! Take it back! Take it back, you palavering old crow of a catchpole! You have cramped me tight and hauled me to a grave. Take it back, you!"

"Well met, friend," a voice replied, and there was the old leprechaun bowing before him. "Your wish is granted."

True it was. They were standing beside a field of corn ripe and ready, waving and sighing it was. The Gollan could hear once more, he could touch, taste, and smell again, and he could see his own royal king as clear as print on a page of history hurrying down the road towards them.

"What else can I do for you?" asked the little red-haired man.

"I fancy," said The Gollan, jerking his thumb towards the king, "he is running to ask me for a large great army."

"You shall have that," said the leprechaun, vanishing away at the king's approach.

"Gollan," the king says, "I want a large great army."

"Yes, Sir," says The Gollan. "Will you have the grenadiers, the bombardiers, or men of the broad-sword?"

He said he would have the bombardiers.

Well, The Gollan made a pass of his hand over that field of corn, and the standing stalks at once began to whistle and sway sideways. Before you could blink a lash there they were, 50,000 men and noblemen, all marking time, all dressed to glory with great helmets and eager for battle.

"Gollan," says the king, "will you undertake the command of this my noble army?"

"I will that, Sir."

"Lead on, then," says the king, and "may the blood of calamity never splash upon one single rib of the whole lot of you."

Which, it is good to say, it never did. The Gollan then marched them straightway to battle by the shore of the lake.

"Get ready now," cried General Gollan, "here comes the artillery with their big guns!"

The bombardiers began to prepare themselves and first gave a blast on their trumpets, but the enemy got ready sooner and fired off a blast on all their culverins, mortars, and whatnot. Ah, what a roar they let out of that huge and fatal cannonade! It would have frightened the trunk of a tree out of its own bark, and at the mere sound of it every man of General Gollan's army toppled to the earth like corn that is cut, never to rise again.

"What is it and all!" cried the distracted Gollan. "Is this another joke of that palavering old crow of a catchpole? By the soul of my aunty!" he exclaimed, as he surveyed his exposed position amid all those fallen bombardiers, so neat, so gallant, so untimely dead, "By the soul of my aunty I think I'd rather be invisible now!"

In a twink he was invisible once more, and his five senses gone again; but none of his friends ever had time to enquire what became of him because the conquering general painfully exterminated them all.

Unseen, unknown, the good Gollan lived on for many years in great privation, and when he at last came to die (though nobody knew even about that) he had grown mercifully wise and wrote his own epitaph—though nobody ever saw it:

To choose was my need, but need brooks no choosing.

The Fairy Shoe
Edith Somerville

THERE IS in the southwest of the County Cork, a wild, almost uninhabited, and very beautiful tract of mountain country, that extends from Bantry Bay into Kerry, and onwards; Glengariff is its central point, and Castletown Bere Haven (once, not long ago, an important station of the British Fleet) is another outpost of civilization, planted in the wilderness near the mouth of Bantry Bay. Anyone who has read Froude's historical romance, *The Two Chiefs of Dunboy*, will remember that one of them was O'Sullivan Bere, lord of all that country, and O'Sullivan's country is still the name it goes by. This story begins later than the time of the two Chiefs, in the year 1836, to be exact, nearly a hundred years ago, when, it may safely be taken for granted, civilization among these mountains was only such as had survived from the legendary times of Irish culture. One still can meet with beautiful manners among the "mountainy" people. Courteous to the stranger, self-respecting, unhandicapped by any consciousness of such superficials as bare feet or rags. In 1836 Castletown Bere was a very small and primitive village, untouched even by such civilization as Bantry knew. A very old gentleman who, as Coroner, had occasionally to make his way into the mountains, has told me that he had seen a cabin built around a single big block of stone, which served as a table, and was the only furniture that the place possessed. (But primitive as it is, that wild country has a long history, and it is well known that it was out somewhere on that desolate coast that the Prophet Jeremiah landed when he brought Pharaoh's daughter with him to Ireland. And this must be true, because every second boy in the County of Cork answers to the name of

Jerry!)

In, or near, the village of Castletown, at this time, 1836, there lived a doctor named Armstrong. To him, one morning early, came a man of the hills, a "mountainy man," to say his wife was ill, and to ask for help. The man told the Doctor that he had made all the haste he could, and had come over the mountains by as near a way as he could make. And then, I can imagine, with shyness and some hesitation, he showed the Doctor a little shoe—a tiny little bit of a shoe, not quite three inches long. He said it was in the dawning that he had seen it on the grass, on a high pass in those lonesome hills. He didn't much care for the little shoe. But it might bring luck, and he hadn't liked to leave it, lying on the short mountain grass; but again, it mightn't. I can imagine him turning it about uncomfortably, before he ventured to hint that it must have been dropped by one of the Good People—a Cluricaun maybe, a lad that if you could catch a hold of him, you might make him show you where he had his crock of gold hidden. Cluricauns (or Leprechauns) are the fairies' cobblers, "and I wouldn't doubt," says the mountainy man, "but this lad was mending the shoe for one o' them, and he heard meself coming, and he legged it away then and left the brogueeen after him!"

Some such explanation, I expect, the man offered the Doctor, and then, with all the satisfaction one feels in making a handsome present of something that one wants to get rid of, he presented the Doctor with the little shoe.

This is the true history of the entrance of the Fairy Shoe into mortal society. The Doctor gave it to his sister, who married Judge Fitzhenry Townshend, who was my Grandfather's first cousin, and she left it, with its history carefully set down and attested, to her daughter, and it came at last to her great-granddaughter, and she—like the mountainy man—didn't altogether fancy it, so she gave it to my sister (and I think it has brought luck instead of taking it away).

•   •   •   •   •

The little shoe came with us across the Atlantic. It seemed to us that in America, if anywhere, we should meet people with open minds, not afraid to be interested in what they could not explain.

And we found that we had not been mistaken. The Fairy Shoe had, everywhere, a reception that was at once enthusiastic and respectful. But it was at our High Brow parties at Yale that it received the discerning and unprejudiced examination to which it is justly entitled. Let me try to describe it.

It is made of black—or what once may have been black—leather as fine and nearly as thin as silk; and yet it is real leather, that looks like the strong leather of which our countrymen's brogues are made, were it seen through a diminishing glass. It is shaped like a brogue, but is unnaturally narrow for its length. The sole at its widest is no more than three-quarters of an inch wide, while it is two-and-three-quarters inches long. (How slim and slender must be the fairy feet!)

There are little holes in the "uppers" for laces. The workmanship is incredibly fine. There are signs of wear at the heel, which is wrinkled a little, and the sole is dented, no doubt with the rocks of the mountains, where its wearer "fleeted the time away as in the Golden Age!" (For those who do not know what a "brogue" is like, this drawing is as accurate as I could make it, and is the exact size of the shoe.)

The impressive fact about the exhibition at Yale of this "enigma from the world antique" was the cool and courageous acceptance of it as a problem for which a solution might or

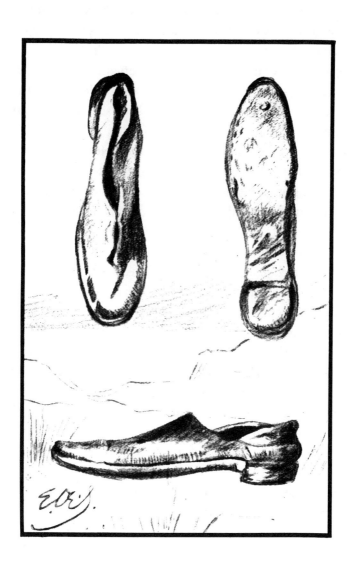

might not be found. It occurred to no one to dismiss with derision what could not be explained. No one made the suggestion that it was a doll's shoe—or a baby's. (A doll's shoe, found on a desolate mountain pass, forty miles from any town! A baby's shoe made of leather, and not an inch wide!) These conjectures have many times been the refuges of the destitute in intelligence, but Yale offered no such futile insults to the Cluricaun's brogue! Five, it may have been six, men of learning, occupants of those Seats of the Mighty, the Chairs of the University, placed themselves round a table in the center of which sat the little shoe in solitary state, complacently challenging investigation, and not even that Professor whose especial subject was the fancies and follies of Folklore, could suggest a solution that conformed with the facts. Wisdom has sometimes the courage to admit itself baffled.

I have talked to an illiterate Kerry peasant who owned a small farm deep in the mountains above Killarney. His farm is beside a little lake, with (so I had been told) a fairy island on it, and—so I had been further told—"anyone that'd land on it'd get a sthroke." I asked the farmer if he had ever seen the fairies. He said no, he hadn't seen them himself. "But," he said, "my father seen them, and they that high" (he indicated about two feet from the ground), "and with red caps on them. And"—he added—"they having green faces."

Now it is a singular fact that a short time before this, I had read an article in "Light," in which it was said that Sir Arthur Conan Doyle had formed the opinion that there were two tribes of fairies, and one tribe had blue faces, and the other green.

A lady who lives at Glengariff has told me of the reluctance of one of her workmen to cut timber in a certain wood, because he said the fairies came about him there, and frightened him. And she has shown me a picture, painted while he was her guest, by that Irish poet, and painter, and seer, who is best known by the mystic initials A. E., in which a fairy boat, with fairy beings in it, is drifting on the waters of that most lovely harbor; and his friend and hostess said he had painted it from life.

I have had the pleasure of meeting A. E.; he told me how, on the Dublin mountains, he had made many sketches of the beings he had seen there; he said that he had shown these to an old woman in the County Mayo (who also had "the Sight"), and she had picked out some of his drawings, rejecting others, as being pictures like the fairies she had seen.

Moreover—this for the incredulous of the New World—a visitor to Ireland from the States, has given me a full account of how she and three friends were all put astray on a mountain in Mayo by "Horns of Elfland, faint blowing"; and in the air around them laughter and crying, where was no one to laugh or cry; and twice by little figures, far away, beckoning to them, for whom my friend and her companions searched, believing they might be lost children, and found not.

•　　　•　　　•　　　•　　　•

One more incident in the career of the Fairy Shoe I must give, and I will then undertake not to recur to the subject.

The experiment of seeing what a psychometrist could make of it was suggested, and wrapped in a disguising swaddling of paper, it was given to one of those on whom the mysterious gift has been bestowed of receiving from some inanimate object intimations of its past. In this case the resulting emotions were vague and troubled. The Sensitive spoke disquietedly of a Strange People, of warriors, of fighting, and of horses often, of galloping horses—bewilderment—nothing definite.

Had the two Chiefs of Dunboy ridden out against each other over that high mountain pass? Or were the galloping horses fairy horses, made of bulrushes—as is the fairy way—and ridden to battle by warring tribes of a strange people, some with blue faces, and some with green faces?

Darby O'Gill and the Leprechaun
Herminie Kavanagh

THE NEWS that Darby O'Gill had spint six months with the Good People spread fast and far and wide.

At fair or hurlin' or market he would be backed be a crowd agin some convaynient wall and there for hours men, women, and childher, with jaws dhroppin' and eyes bulgin'd, stand ferninst him listening to half-frightened questions or to bould, mystarious answers.

Alway, though, one bit of wise adwise inded his discoorse: "Nayther make nor moil nor meddle with the fairies," Darby'd say. "If you're going along the lonely boreen at night and you hear, from some fairy fort, a sound of fiddles, or of piping, or of sweet woices singing, or of little feet patthering in the dance, don't turn your head, but say your prayers an' hould on your way. The pleasures the Good People'll share with you have a sore sorrow hid in them, an' the gifts they'll offer are only made to break hearts with."

Things went this a-way till one day in the market, over among the cows, Maurteen Cavanaugh, the schoolmasther—a cross-faced, argifying ould man he was—conthradicted Darby pint blank. "Stay a bit," says Maurteen, catching Darby by the coat-collar. "You forget about the little fairy cobbler, the Leprechaun," he says. "You can't deny that to catch the Leprechaun is great luck entirely. If one only fix the glance of his eye on the cobbler, that look makes the fairy a presner—one can do anything with him as long as a human look covers the little lad and he'll give the favors of three wishes to buy his freedom," says Maurteen.

At that Darby, smiling high and knowledgeable, made answer over the heads of the crowd.

"God help your sinse, honest man!" he says. "Around the favors of thim same three wishes is a bog of thricks an' cajolories and con-ditions that'll defayt the wisest.

"First of all, if the look be taken from the little cobbler for as much as the wink of an eye, he's gone forever," he says. "Man alive, even when he does grant the favors of the three wishes, you're not safe, for, if you tell anyone you've seen the Leprechaun, the favors melt like snow, or if you make a fourth wish that day—whiff! they turn to smoke. Take my advice— nayther make nor moil nor meddle with the fairies."

"Thrue for ye," spoke up long Pether McCarthy, siding in with Darby. "Didn't Barney McBride, on his way to early mass one May morning, catch the fairy cobbler sewing an' workin' away under a hedge. 'Have a pinch of snuff, Barney agra,' says the Leprechaun, handing up the little snuff-box. But, mind ye, when my poor Barney bint to take a thumb an' finger full, what did the little villain do but fling the box, snuff and all, into Barney's face. An' thin, whilst the poor lad was winkin' and blinkin', the Leprechaun gave one leap and was lost in the reeds.

"Thin, again, there was Peggy O'Rourke, who captured him fair an' square in a hawthorn-bush. In spite of his wiles she wrung from him the favors of the three wishes. Knowing, of course, that if she towld of what had happened to her the spell was broken and the wishes wouldn't come thrue, she hurried home, aching and longing to in some way find from her husband Andy what wishes she'd make.

"Throwing open her own door, she said, 'What would ye wish for most in the world, Andy dear? Tell me an' your wish'll

come thrue,' says she. A peddler was crying his wares out in the
lane. 'Lanterns, tin lanterns!' cried the peddler. 'I wish I had one
of thim lanterns,' says Andy, careless, and bendin' over to get a
coal for his pipe, when, lo and behold, there was the lantern in
his hand.

"Well, so vexed was Peggy that one of her fine wishes should
be wasted on a palthry tin lantern, that she lost all patience with
him. 'Why thin, bad scran to you!' says she—not mindin' her
own words —'I wish the lantern was fastened to the ind of your
nose!'

"The word wasn't well out of her mouth till the lantern *was*
hung swinging from the ind of Andy's nose in a way that the wit
of man couldn't loosen. It took the third and last of Peggy's
wishes to relayse Andy."

"Look at that, now!" cried a dozen voices from the admiring
crowd. "Darby said so from the first."

Well, after a time people used to come from miles around to
see Darby and sit undher the sthraw-stack beside the stable to
adwise with our hayro about their most important business—
what was the best time for the settin' of hins, or what was good
to cure colic in childher, an' things like that.

Any man so parsecuted with admiration an' hayrofication
might aisily feel his chest swell out a bit, so it's no wondher that
Darby set himself up for a knowledgeable man.

He took to talkin' slow an' shuttin' one eye whin he listened,
and he walked with a knowledgeable twist to his chowlders. He
grew monsthrously fond of fairs and public gatherings where
people made much of him, and he lost every ounce of liking he
ever had for hard worruk.

Things wint on with him in this way from bad to worse, and
where it would have inded no man knows, if one unlucky
morning he hadn't rayfused to bring in a creel of turf his wife

Bridget had axed him to fetch her. The unfortunate man said it was no work for the likes of him.

The last word was still on Darby's lips whin he rayalized his mistake, an' he'd have given the world to have the sayin' back again.

For a minute you could have heard a pin dhrop. Bridget, instead of being in a hurry to begin at him, was crool dayliberate. She planted herself in the door, her two fists on her hips, an' her lips shut.

The look Julius Sayser'd trow at a servant-girl he'd caught stealing sugar from the rile cupboard was the glance she waved up and down from Darby's toes to his head, and from his head to his brogues agin.

Thin she began an' talked steady as a fall of hail that has now an' then a bit of lightning an' tunder mixed in it.

The knowledgeable man stood purtendin' to brush his hat and tryin' to look brave, but the heart inside of him was meltin' like butther.

Bridget began aisily be carelessly mentioning a few of Darby's best known wakenesses. Afther that she took up some of them not so well known, being ones Darby himself had sayrious doubts about having at all. But on these last she was more savare than on the first. Through it all he daren't say a word—he only smiled lofty and bitther.

'Twas but natural next for Bridget to explain what a poor crachure her husband was the day she got him, an what she might have been if she had married ayther one of the six others who had axed her. The step for her was a little one, thin, to the shortcomings and misfortunes of his blood relaytions, which she follyed back to the blaggardisms of his fourth cousin, Phelim McFadden.

Even in his misery poor Darby couldn't but marvel at her

wondherful memory.

By the time she began talking of her own family, and especially about her Aunt Honoria O'Shaughnessy, who had once shook hands with a Bishop, and who in the rebellion of '98 had trun a brick at a Lord Liftenant, whin he was riding by, Darby was as wilted and as forlorn-looking as a roosther caught out in the winther rain.

He lost more pride in those few minutes than it had taken months to gather an' hoard. It kept falling in great drops from his forehead.

Just as Bridget was lading up to what Father Cassidy calls a pur-roar-ration—that being the part of your wife's discoorse whin, after telling you all she's done for you, and all she's stood from your relaytions, she breaks down and cries, and so smothers you entirely—just as she was coming to that, I say, Darby scrooged his caubeen down on his head, stuck his fingers in his two ears, and, making one grand rush through the door, bolted as fast as his legs could carry him down the road toward Sleive-na-mon Mountains.

Bridget stood on the step looking afther him, too surprised for a word. With his fingers still in his ears, so that he couldn't hear her commands to turn back, he ran without stopping till he came to the willow-tree near Joey Hooligan's forge. There he slowed down to fill his lungs with the fresh, sweet air.

'Twas one of those warm-hearted, laughing autumn days which steals for a while the bonnet and shawl of the May. The sun, from a sky of feathery whiteness, laned over, telling jokes to the worruld, an' the goold harvest-fields and purple hills, lasy and continted, laughed back at the sun. Even the blackbird flying over the haw-tree looked down an' sang to those below, "God save all here"; an' the linnet from her bough answered back quick an' sweet, "God save you kindly, sir !"

With such pleasant sight and sounds an' twitterings at every side, our hayro didn't feel the time passing till he was on top of the first hill of the Sleive-na-mon Mountains, which, as everyone knows, is called the Pig's Head.

It wasn't quite lonesome enough on the Pig's Head, so our hayro plunged into the walley an' climbed the second mountain—the Divil's Pillow where 'twas lonesome and desarted enough to shuit anyone.

Beneath the shade of a tree, for the days was warm, he set himself down in the long, sweet grass, lit his pipe, and let his mind go free. But, as he did, his thoughts rose together like a flock of frightened, angry pheasants, an' whirred back to the owdacious things Bridget had said about his relations.

Wasn't she the mendageous, humbrageous woman, he thought, to say such things about as illegant stock, as the O'Gills and the O'Gradys?

Why, Wullum O'Gill, Darby's uncle, at that minute, was head butler at Castle Brophy, and was known far an' wide as being one of the foinest scholars an' as having the most beautiful pair of legs in all Ireland!

This same Wullum O'Gill had tould Bridget in Darby's own hearing, on a day when the three were going through the great picture-gallery at Castle Brophy, that the O'Gills at one time had been Kings in Ireland.

Darby never since could raymember whether this time was before the flood or afther the flood. Bridget said it was durin' the flood, but surely that sayin' was nonsinse.

Howsumever, Darby knew his Uncle Wullum was right, for he often felt in himself the signs of greatness. And now as he sat alone on the grass, he said out loud:

"If I had me rights I'd be doing nothing all day long but sittin' on a throne, an' playin' games of forty-five with the Lord

Liftenant an' some of me generals. There never was a lord that likes good ating or dhrinking betther nor I, or who hates worse to get up airly in the morning. That last disloike I'm tould is a great sign entirely of gentle blood the worruld over," says he.

As for the wife's people, the O'Hagans an' the O'Shaughnessys, well—they were no great shakes, he said to himself, at laste so far as looks were concerned. All the handsomeness in Darby's childher came from his own side of the family. Even Father Cassidy said the childher took afther the O'Gills .

"If I were rich," said Darby, to a lazy ould bumble-bee who was droning an' tumbling in front of him, "I'd have a castle like Castle Brophy, with a great picture-gallery in it. On one wall I'd put the picture of the O'Gills and the O'Gradys, and on the wall ferninst them I'd have the O'Hagans an' the O'Shaughnessys."

At that ideah his heart bubbled in a new and fierce deloight. "Bridget's people," he says agin, scowling at the bee, "would look four times as common as they raylly are, whin they were compared in that way with my own relations. An' whenever Bridget got rampageous I'd take her in and show her the difference betwixt the two clans, just to punish her, so I would."

How long the lad sat that way warming the cowld thoughts of his heart with drowsy, pleasant dhrames an' misty longings he don't rightly know, whin—tack, tack, tack, tack, came the busy sound of a little hammer from the other side of a fallen oak.

"Be jingo!" he says to himself with a start, "'tis the Leprechaun that's in it."

In a second he was on his hands an' knees, the tails of his coat flung across his back, an' he crawling softly toward the sound of the hammer. Quiet as a mouse he lifted himself up on the mossy log to look over, and there before his two popping eyes was a sight of wondheration.

Sitting on a white stone an' working away like fury,

hammering pegs into a little red shoe, half the size of your thumb, was a bald-headed ould cobbler of about twice the hoight of your hand. On the top of a round, snub nose was perched a pair of horn-rimmed spectacles, an' a narrow fringe of iron-gray whuskers grew undher his stubby chin. The brown leather apron he wore was so long that it covered his green knee-breeches an' almost hid the knitted gray stockings.

The Leprechaun—for it was he indade—as he worked, mumbled an' mutthered in great discontent:

"Oh, haven't I the hard, hard luck," he said. "I'll never have thim done in time for her to dance in tonight. So, thin, I'll be kilt entirely," says he. "Was there ever another quane of the fairies as wearing on shoes an' brogues an' dancin' slippers? Haven't I the—" Looking up, he saw Darby.

"The top of the day to you, dacint man!" says the cobbler, jumpin' up. Giving a sharp cry, he pinted quick at Darby's stomach. "But, wirra, wirra, what's that wooly, ugly thing you have crawling an' creepin' on your weskit?" he said, purtendin' to be all excited.

"Sorra thing on my weskit," answered Darby, cool as ice, "or anywhere else that'll make me take my two bright eyes off'n you—not for a second," says he.

"Well! Well! will you look at that, now?" laughed the cobbler. "Mark how quick an' handy he took me up! Will you have a pinch of snuff, clever man?" he axed, houlding up the little box.

"Is it the same snuff you gave Barney McBride a while ago?" axed Darby, sarcastic. "Lave off your foolishness," says our hayro, growin' fierce, "and grant me at once the favors of the three wishes, or I'll have you smoking like a herring in my own chimney before nightfall," says he.

At that the Leprechaun, seeing that he but wasted time on so knowledgeable a man as Darby O'Gill, surrendhered, and

granted the favors of the three wishes.

"What is it you ask?" says the cobbler, himself turning on a sudden very sour an' sullen.

"First an' foremost," says Darby, "I want a home of my ansisthers, an' it must be a castle like Castle Brophy, with pictures of my kith an' kin on the wall, and then facing them pictures of my wife Bridget's kith an' kin on the other wall."

"That favor I give ye, that wish I grant ye," says the fairy, making the shape of a castle on the ground with his awl.

"What next?" he grunted.

"I want goold enough for me an' my generations to enjoy in grandeur the place forever."

"Always the goold," sneered the little man, bending to dhraw with his awl on the turf the shape of a purse.

"Now for your third and last wish. Have a care!"

"I want the castle set on this hill—the Divils Pillow—where we two stand," says Darby. Then sweeping with his arm, he says, "I want the land about to be my demesne."

The Leprechaun stuck his awl on the ground. "That wish I give you, that wish I grant you," he says. With that he straightened himself up, and grinning most aggravaytin' the while, he looked Darby over from top to toe. "You're a foine, knowledgeable man, but have a care of the fourth wish!" says he.

Bekase there was more of a challenge than friendly warning in what the small lad said, Darby snapped his fingers at him an' cried:

"Have no fear, little man! If I got all Ireland ground for making a fourth wish, however small, before midnight I'd not make it. I'm going home now to fetch Bridget an' the childher, and the only fear or unaisiness I have is that you'll not keep your word, so as to have the castle here ready before us when I come back."

"Oho! I'm not to be thrusted, amn't I?" screeched the little lad, flaring into a blazing passion. He jumped upon the log that was betwixt them, and with one fist behind his back shook the other at Darby.

"You ignorant, suspicious-minded blaggard!" says he. "How dare the likes of you say the likes of that to the likes of me!" cried the cobbler. "I'd have you to know," he says, " that I had a repitation for truth an' voracity ayquil if not shuperior to the best, before you were born!" he shouted. "I'll take no high talk from a man that's afraid to give words to his own wife if whin she's in a tantrum!" says the Leprechaun.

"It's aisy to know you're not a married man," says Darby, mighty scornful, "bekase if you—"

The lad stopped short, forgetting what he was going to say in his surprise an' aggaytation, for the far side of the mountain was waving up an' down before his eyes like a great green blanket that is being shook by two women, while at the same time high spots of turf on the hillside toppled sidewise to level themselves up with the low places. The enchantment had already begun to make things ready for the castle. A dozen foine trees that stood in a little grove bent their heads quickly together, and thin by some inwisible hand they were plucked up by the roots an' dhropped aside much the same as a man might grasp a handful of weeds an' fling them from his garden.

The ground under the knowledgeable man's feet began to rumble an' heave. He waited for no more. With a cry that was half of gladness an' half of fear, he turned on his heel an' started on a run down into the walley, leaving the little cobbler standing on the log, shouting abuse after him an' ballyraggin' him as he ran.

So excited was Darby that, going up the Pig's Head, he was

nearly run over by a crowd of great brown building stones which were moving down slow an' ordherly like a flock of driven sheep—but they moved without so much as bruising a blade of grass or bendin' a twig, as they came.

Only once, and that at the top of the Pig's Head, he trew a look back.

The Divil's Pillow was in a great commotion; a whirlwind was sweeping over it—whether of dust or of mist he couldn't tell.

Afther this, Darby never looked back again or to the right or the left of him, but kept straight on till he found himself, panting and pufflng, at his own kitchen door. 'Twas tin minutes before he could spake, but at last, whin he tould Bridget to make ready herself and the childher to go up to the Divil's Pillow with him, for once in her life that raymarkable woman, without axing, How comes it so, What rayson have you, or Why should I do it, set to work washing the childer's faces.

Maybe she dabbed a little more soap in their eyes than was needful, for 'twas a habit she had; though this time if she did, not a whimper broke from the little hayros. For the matther of that, not one word, good, bad or indifferent, did herself spake till the whole family were trudging down the lane two by two, marching like sojers.

As they came near the first hill along its sides the evening twilight turned from purple to brown, and at the top of the Pig's Head the darkness of a black night swooped suddenly down on them. Darby hurried on a step or two ahead, an' resting his hand upon the large rock that crowns the hill, looked anxiously over to the Divil's Pillow. Although he was ready for something foine, yet the greatness of the foineness that met his gaze knocked the breath out of him.

Across the deep walley, and on top of the second mountain,

he saw lined against the evening sky the roof of an imminse castle, with towers an' parrypets an' battlements. Undher the towers a thousand sullen windows glowed red in the black walls. Castle Brophy couldn't hould a candle to it.

"Behold!" says Darby, flinging out his arm, and turning to his wife, who had just come up—"behold the castle of my ansisthers who were my forefathers!"

"How," says Bridget, quick and scornful—"how could your aunt's sisters be your four fathers?"

What Darby was going to say to her he don't just raymember, for at that instant from the right-hand side of the mountain came a cracking of whips, a rattling of wheels, an' the rush of horses, and, lo and behold! a great dark coach with flashing lamps, and drawn by four coal-black horses, dashed up the hill and stopped beside them. Two shadowy men were on the driver's box.

"Is this Lord Darby O'Gill?" axed one of them, in a deep, muffled woice. Before Darby could reply, Bridget took the words out of his mouth.

"It is!" she cried, in a kind of a half cheer, "an' Lady O'Gill an' the childher."

"Then hurry up!" says the coachman. "Your supper's gettin' cowld."

Without waiting for anyone Bridget flung open the carriage door, an' pushin' Darby aside jumped in among the cushions. Darby, his heart sizzlin' with vexation at her audaciousness, lifted in one after another the childher, and then got in himself.

He couldn't undherstand at all the change in his wife, for she had always been the odherliest, modestist woman in the parish.

Well, he'd no sooner shut the door than crack went the whip, the horses gave a spring, the carriage jumped, and down the hill they went. For fastness there was never another carriage-ride like that before nor since. Darby hildt tight with both hands to the window, his face pressed against the glass. He couldn't tell whether the horses were only flying or whether the coach was falling down the hill into the walley. By the hollow feeling in his stomach he thought they were falling. He was striving to think of some prayers when there came a terrible jolt which sint his two heels against the roof an' his head betwixt the cushions. As he righted himself the wheels began to grate on a graveled road, an' plainly they were dashing up the side of the second mountain.

Even so, they couldn't have gone far whin the carriage dhrew up in a flurry, an' he saw through the gloom a high iron gate being slowly opened.

"Pass on," said a voice from somewhere in the shadows; "their supper's getting cowld."

As they flew undher the great archway, Darby had a glimpse of the thing which had opened the gate, and had said their supper was getting cowld. It was standing on its hind legs—in the darkness he couldn't be quite sure as to its shape, but it was ayther a Bear or a Loin.

His mind was in a pondher about this when, with a swirl an' a bump, the carriage stopped another time, an' now it stood before a broad flight of stone steps which led up to the main door of the castle. Darby, half afraid, peering out through the darkness, saw a square of light high above him which came from the open hall door. Three sarvants in livery stood waiting on the thrashol.

"Make haste, make haste!" says one, in a doleful voice; "their supper's gettin' cowld."

Hearing these words, Bridget imagetly bounced out, an' was halfway up the steps before Darby could ketch her an' hould her till the childher came up.

"I never in all my life saw her so owdacious," he says, half cryin', an' linkin' her arm to keep her back, an' thin, with the childher following two by two, according to size, the whole family payraded up the steps, till Darby, with a gasp of deloight, stopped on the thrashol of a splendid hall. From a high ceiling hung great flags from every nation an' domination, which swung and swayed in the dazzlin' light. Two lines of men and maid servants dhressed in silks an' satins an' brocades, stood facing aich other, bowing an' smiling an' wavin' their hands in welcome. The two lines stretched down to the goold stairway at the far ind of the hall. For half of one minute Darby, every eye in his head as big as a tay-cup, stood hesitaytin'. Thin he said, "Why should it flutther me? Arrah, ain't it all mine? Aren't all these people in me pay? I'll engage it's a pritty penny all this grandeur is costing me to keep up this minute." He trew out his chist. "Come on, Bridget!" he says; "let's go into the home of my ansisthers."

Howandever, scarcely had he stepped into the beautiful place whin two pipers with their pipes, two fiddlers with their fiddles, two flute-players with their flutes, an' they dhressed in scarlet an' goold, stepped out in front of him, and thus to maylodius music the family proudly marched down the hall, climbed up the goolden stairway at its ind, an' thin turned to enter the biggest room Darby had ever seen.

Something in his sowl whuspered that this was the picture-gallery.

"Be the powers of Pewther!" says the knowledgeable man to himself, "I wouldn't be in Bridget's place this minute for a hatful of money! Wait, oh just wait, till she has to compare her own relations with my own foine people! I know how she'll feel, but I wondher what she'll say," he says.

The thought that all the unjust things, all the unraysonable things Bridget had said about his kith an' kin were just going to be disproved and turned against herself, made him proud an' almost happy.

But wirrasthrue! He should have raymembered his own adwise not to make nor moil nor meddle with the fairies, for here he was to get the first hard welt from the little Leprechaun.

It was the picture-gallery sure enough, but how terribly different everything was from what the poor lad expected. There on the left wall, grand an' noble, shone the pictures of Bridget's people. Of all the well-dressed, handsome, proud-appearing persons in the whole worruld, the O'Hagans an' the O'Shaughnessys would compare with the best. This was a hard enough crack, though a crushinger knock was to come. Ferninst them on the right wall glowered the O'Gills and the O'Gradys, and of all the ragged, sheep-stealing, hangdog-looking villains one ever saw in jail or out of jail, it was Darby's kindred.

The place of honor on the right wall was given to Darby's fourth cousin, Phelem McFadden, an' he was painted with a pair of handcuffs on him. Wullum O'Gill had a squint in his right eye, and his thin legs bowed like hoops on a barrel.

If you have ever at night been groping your way through a dark room, and got a sudden, hard bump on the forehead from the edge of the door, you can undherstand the feelings of the knowledgeable man.

"Take that picture out!" he said, hoarsely, as soon as he could speak. "An' will someone kindly inthrojuice me to the man who med it? Bekase," he says, "I intend to take his life! There was never a crass-eyed O'Gill since the world began," says he.

Think of his horror an' surprise whin he saw the left eye of Wullum O'Gill twist itself slowly over toward his nose and squint worse than the right eye.

Purtending not to see this, an' hoping no one else did, Darby fiercely led the way over to the other wall.

Fronting him stood the handsome picture of Honoria O'Shaughnessy, an' she dhressed in a shuit of tin clothes like the knights of ould used to wear—armor I think they calls it.

She hildt a spear in her hand with a little flag on the blade, an' her smile was proud and high.

"Take that likeness out, too," says Darby, very spiteful; "that's not a dacint shuit of clothes for any woman to wear!"

The next minute you might have knocked him down with a feather, for the picture of Honoria O'Shaughnessy opened its mouth an' stuck out its tongue at him.

"The supper's getting cowld, the supper's getting cowld!" someone cried at the other ind of the picture gallery. Two big doors were swung open, an' glad enough was our poor hayro to folly the musicianers down to the room where the ating an' drinking were to be thransacted.

This was a little room with lots of looking-glasses, and it was bright with a thousand candles, and white with the shining-ist marble. On the table was biled beef an' reddishes an' carrots an' roast mutton an' all kinds of important ating an' drinking. Beside there stood fruits an' sweets an'—but, sure, what is the use in talkin'?

A high-backed chair stood ready for aich of the family, an' 'twas a lovely sight to see them all whin they were sitting there—Darby at the head, Bridget at the foot, the childher—the poor little paythriarchs —sitting bolt upright on aich side, with a bewigged and befrilled serving-man standing haughty behind every chair.

The atin' and dhrinkin' would have begun at once—in throth there was already a bit of biled beef on Darby's plate—only that he spied a little silver bell beside him. Sure, 'twas one like those the quality keep to ring whin they want more hot wather for their punch, but it puzzled the knowledgeable man, and 'twas the beginning of his misfortune.

"I wondher," he thought, "if 'tis here for the same raison as
the bell is at the Curragh races—do they ring this one so that all
at the table will start ating and dhrinking fair, an' no one will
have the advantage, or is it," he says to himself agin, "to ring
whin the head of the house thinks everyone has had enough.
Haven't the quality quare ways! I'll be a long time learning
them," he says.

He sat silent and puzzling an' staring at the biled beef on his
plate, afeard to start in without ringing the bell, an' dhreadin' to
risk ringing it. The grand sarvants towered cowldly on every
side, their chins tilted, but they kep' throwing over their
chowlders glances so scornful and haughty that Darby shivered
at the thought of showing any uncultivaytion.

While our hayro sat thus in unaisy contimplation an'
smouldherin' mortification an' flurried hesitaytion, a
powdhered head was poked over his chowlder, and a soft,
beguiling voice said, "Is there anything else you'd wish for?"

The foolish lad twisted in his chair, opened his mouth to
spake, and gave a look at the bell; shame rushed to his cheeks,
he picked up a bit of the biled beef on his fork, an' to consale
his turpitaytion gave the misfortunit answer:

"I'd wish for a pinch of salt, if you plaze," says he.

'Twas no sooner said than came the crash. Oh, tunderation an'
murdheration, what a roaring crash it was! The lights winked
out together at a breath an' left a pitchy, throbbing darkness.
Overhead and to the sides was a roaring, smashing, crunching
noise, like the ocean's madness when the winthry storm breaks
agin the Kerry shore, an' in that roar was mingled the tearing
and the splitting of the walls and the fading of the chimneys.
But through all this confusion could be heard the shrill,
laughing woice of the Leprechaun. "The clever man med his

fourth grand wish" it howled.

Darby—a thousand wild woices screaming an' mocking above him—was on his back kicking and squirming and striving to get up, but some load hilt him down, an' something bound his eyes shut.

"Are you kilt, Bridget asthore?" he cried; "Where are the childher?" he says.

Instead of answer there suddenly flashed a fierce an' angry silence, an' its quickness frightened the lad more than all the wild confusion before.

'Twas a full minute before he dared to open his eyes to face the horrors which he felt were standing about him; but when courage enough to look came, all he saw was the night-covered mountain, a purple sky, and a thin, new moon, with one trembling goold star a hand's space above its bosom.

Darby struggled to his feet. Not a stone of the castle was left, not a sod of turf but what was in its ould place; every sign of the little cobbler's work had melted like April snow. The very trees Darby had seen pulled up by the roots that same afternoon now stood a waving blur below the new moon, an' a nightingale was singing in their branches. A cricket chirped lonesomely on the same fallen log which had hidden the Leprechaun.

"Bridget! Bridget!" Darby called agin an' agin. Only a sleepy owl on a distant hill answered.

A shivering thought jumped into the boy's bewildered sowl— maybe the Leprechaun had stolen Bridget an' the childher.

The poor man turned, and for the last time darted down into the night-filled walley.

Not a pool in the road he waited to go around, not a ditch in his path he didn't leap over, but ran as he never ran before till he raiched his own front door.

His heart stood still as he peeped through the window. There

were the childher croodled around Bridget, who sat with the
youngest asleep in her lap before the fire, rocking back an'
forth, an' she crooning a happy, continted baby-song.

Tears of gladness crept into Darby's eyes as he looked in
upon her. "God bless her!" he says to himself. "She's the flower
of the O'Hagans and the O'Shaughnessys, and she's a proud
feather in the caps of the O'Gills and the O'Gradys."

'Twas well he had this happy thought to cheer him as he lifted
the door-latch, for the manest of all the little cobbler's spiteful
thricks waited in the house to meet Darby—nayther Bridget nor
the childher raymembered a single thing of all that had
happened to them during the day. They were willing to make
their happydavitts that they had been no farther than their own
petatie-patch since morning.

Index

A. E., 105

Banshees, 25
Beer, heath, 32
Brian Boru, 40

Cluricauns: about, 11, 15, 28, 100; of Oilean na Glas, 25; stories about, 62 passim, 100 passim
Cock crow, 75
Crocks, treasure, 11, 25, 34, 77, 88

Danes, 25, 32
Doyle, Arthur Conan, 104
Dudeens, 24

Fairies: 24-25, 30, 35, 46, 48, 82, 101 passim, 107; blue and green faces of, 104, 106
Fairy dancing, 24
Far Darrigs; about, 11, 28-30; stories about, 29, 30, 71 passim

Ghosts, 56
"God bless us," antidote to leprechaun magic, 40, 41, 42

Horses, bulrush, 38, 39, 40, 106
Hyde, Douglas, 11

Kidnapping, fairies and, 82

Ladyday, 31
Leprechauns: about, 11, 12-23, 24-27, 100, 107 passim, 114; ancestry of, 12, 26; capturing, 16, 17, 18-19, 20-21, 25-26, 33-34, 76-78, 88, 114; domesticity of, 13; dress of, 11, 12-13, 14, 24, 88; gold and, 16-17, 18, 20, 21, 24-26, 77; matrimony and, 18, 26; mischief of, 13, 15, 24; names for, 11, 14; schools and, 15; sentimental kindness of, 26, 94; shoemaking and, 87-88; stories about, 16-17, 18-22, 31 passim, 35 passim, 44 passim, 79 passim, 99 passim, 107 passim
Logheryman, 14
Luchryman, 11
Luricawne, 14-15, 16-17
Lurigadawne, 14

Manners, country squire, 65

Poteen, 71
Psychometrists, 105
Purse, magic, 16, 20-21, 26

Rainbows, 25
Red Man. See Far Darrig

Salutation, Gaelic and fairy, 79
Shee of Croghan Conghaile, 85, 89
Shoes, fairy, 11, 101 passim
Sidhe, 25. See also Fairies
Sneezes, three, as magic, 42
Spirits, good and evil, 12

Wine cellars, 39, 62 passim
Wishes, three, 107, 108, 114, 116